A PERNICIOUS CORRESPONDENCE

LETTERS FROM A DEVIL

BY

SCOTT SCHULEIT

Published by Prevail Press
Copyright © 2021 Scott Schuleit

Cover design by Dawn Davidson
Book Design by Robert Alexander Swanson

ISBN Print: 978-1-948824-23-1
ISBN Digital: 978-1-948824-24-8

DEDICATION

This book is dedicated to the blessed Father, Son, and Holy Spirit.

The LORD reigneth; let the earth rejoice; let the multitude of isles be glad thereof. Clouds and darkness are round about him: righteousness and judgment are the habitation of his throne. A fire goeth before him, and burneth up his enemies round about. His lightnings enlightened the world: the earth saw, and trembled. The hills melted like wax at the presence of the LORD, at the presence of the Lord of the whole earth.

—Psalm 97:1-5

Prologue

Coolness laced the Autumn air; it was slightly sharp, portending a cold winter. I inhaled deeply, taking it in, exhaling slowly. Though a bit chilly, it was a nice night for a walk. Darkness had not yet fully descended. Color was still above the horizon, a deep red and orange-gold brushing clouds, and a band of purple marking the gradual shift between night and day. The light was dissipating, fading before the encroaching dark...

The streets were unusually quiet this evening, devoid of souls. As far as I could see, no matter which direction I turned, I was alone, as if pedestrians had been banished under penalty of death and I had somehow missed the decree. The homes I passed appeared strangely serene. Only a few windows of warm yellow illumination scattered throughout the neighborhood offered any indication of life.

Streetlights lined the avenues, silent, watchful, casting down cones of light, their glass lamps glowing like fireflies, only persistently luminous rather than occasionally flaring. Some contained what appeared to be dark clumps of insects. I wondered, briefly, how insects, lured by light, had managed to breach the lamps, which I took to be sealed.

Walking leisurely, I glanced upwards, finding a rising moon, the whisper of its brightness flowering towards fullness. It seemed unmoored, wandering, adrift amidst a sea of darkness. Beyond it, several stars were emerging, drawn by the allure of the oncoming night, flickering their silver fires.

I turned a corner, moving into an area of abandoned homes and deserted lots. Gnarled, spectral trees haunt the yards, the several dead leaves on their limbs rustling in a light gust of wind. Gaping holes filled with deep shadows marred the frames of the homes. Boarded-up windows appeared as eyeless sockets.

Remnants of light from the gloaming hazed the sky, shades of purple, the trailing skirt of a woman's dress before she finally, gracefully, leaves the room. Within the soft radiance of a streetlight, before turning to walk back the way I came, something caught my eye; a piece of paper partly exposed under a pile of leaves near a drainage grate.

Now, a piece of paper on the street typically holds no luster, but for some reason I walked over to it and crouched down. Retrieving it uncovered an old letter as well as another beneath it. Both were charred at the edges and foul-smelling like sulfur, yet elegantly scripted. Brushing away the pile of leaves clogging the grate revealed, surprisingly, more letters. Heart pounding with a thrill of discovery, I gathered them up, tucked the bundle under my arm, and made my way home.

And there, at my old desk, beneath the glow of a lamp, I read them. As I did, scanning their contents, the thin parchments quivered in my hands, the hair on the back of my neck rose as I realized what I held. My heart and mind raced at the implications, at the import of what was recorded. These were no ordinary letters. They were composed by one Senivilous, apparently a high-ranking demon, to Gorpussel, obviously a demon of lower rank, instructing him on how to tempt a human to sin. Such a strange find must be made public; these letters must be published for the world to see...

Editor's Note

Regarding the letters, it should be noted that an attempt was made by the publisher to place them in the order of their composition, but the precise chronological sequence of the correspondence between Senivilous and Gorpussel could only be partially ascertained. The problem was intensified by the fact that we are not in possession of Gorpussel's letters/reports (known as the Gorpusselian manuscript). There are hopes that these letters, as well as more composed by Senivilous, will be uncovered. The surrounding area near the drainage grate where the Senivilian manuscript was discovered has been, and continues to be, searched.

The main body of the manuscript contains every letter (thirty) where the full text of the writing was legible or easily reconstructed. For scholars in the field and anyone else interested, I have also decided to include the legible parts (twenty-seven) from letters which, due to damage, were not publishable as a whole. These letters were disqualified for publication in the main body of the manuscript because they contained irretrievable words or sections where pieces of the parchment were missing or the script worn away and, in some cases, scorched (perhaps by brimstone). These fragments (the numbering, order, and titles for them are mine) are included in the chapter entitled: **The Senivilian Fragments.**

~~~~~~~~~~~~~~~~

They encourage themselves in an evil matter:
they commune of laying snares privily; they
say, Who shall see them? They search out
iniquities; they accomplish a diligent search:
both the inward thought of every one of
them, and the heart, is deep.

—Psalm 64:5-6

If we have forgotten the name of our God,
or stretched out our hands to a strange
god; Shall not God search this out? For he
knoweth the secrets of the heart.

—Psalm 44:20-21

The heart is deceitful above all things, and
desperately wicked: who can know it? I the
LORD search the heart, I try the reins, even
to give every man according to his ways, and
according to the fruit of his doings.

—Jeremiah 17:9-10

~~~~~~~~~~~~~~~~

A Pernicious Correspondence

Letters from a Devil

Scott Schuleit

Letter #1

Dear Gorpussel,

The boring rhapsodies in your last letter about using "whispers of past sins" against your human subject, warrants a response. First of all, as one of our most common techniques for rendering ineffectual those humans who have been converted by *Him* (that is, souls stolen from us), *guilt* is often subject to overuse as well as misuse. It's easy to become flushed with power and excitement at the way the humans are so responsive to the slightest insinuations of it, but you must always be on guard to avoid pushing your subject too far. Remember to temper your use of guilt lest he become more aware of your existence as well as more mindful of your tactics, diminishing the power we hold through his ignorance. Inflict the silent barrage of guilt when the man is expansive; it's more useful when the animals are cheerful and less vigilant rather than despondent and introspective. Guilt should primarily be used to bring him to despair, opening him up to greater dangers. It's a lead-in, useful for causing them to cast aside their armor, exposing their soft bellies to a sword thrust. By your letter, one would think you had discovered a "magic bullet" rather than a new addition to a growing arsenal of weaponry.

Beyond the topics of when you should use guilt and to what extent, there is also the question of *how* exactly you should approach the two forms of guilt. With regard to the *real* guilt that is rendered by *Him*, in contrast to the fantasy that we or the humans have fabricated, your line of attack involves using your subjects' pride and vanity to encourage either a denial or suppression of its throbbing insistence lest he repent and be restored. When fostering this, work primarily on his emotions. Make him *feel* relieved of his guilt, a false sense of freedom by inducing a careless, cavalier posture regarding sin. Compel him to focus on living the "*Victorious Christian Life*," which in the past involved suffering, but now usually means ignoring indwelling sin and pursuing health, position, power, wealth, comfort and ease. In short, it means embracing the popular doctrine of selfishness rather than self-denial. How they can believe this, in defiance of *that* Book, reason, conscience, and the sufferings of Christians past and present one can only wonder. By the way, also encourage him to abandon that word *sin*; it shouldn't be too hard since we have been successfully persuading them to do so for quite some time. Make him feel learned, "in the know" by using various contemporary alternatives for it such as: *habit*, *problem, psychological condition, orientation, dysfunction, compulsive behavior, coping mechanism, disease, disorder,* and one of my personal favorites, *addiction.* Now it might really be an addiction because sin is addictive, but the point here involves *persistently* substituting a word or phrase for sin that greatly softens its seriousness and, if possible, encourages the subject to see himself as a *victim* or his sin as something normal, natural. The best substitutes remove the volitional element in sin and twist the nature of it altogether such as those that convey the idea that what *that* Book calls "sin" can be explained genetically. The different names we've propagated for that word sin and, consequently, different definitions and approaches to dealing with it, has been one of our greatest victories over the last century.

If you cannot tempt him towards casualness and he actually becomes aware and repents of his sin, work him over with the other extreme of wallowing in his guilt. It must be admitted that the manifestations of suppression are enjoyable to watch, but the actions of those who cling to their guilt are even more amusing. They writhe like worms and the most subtle suggestions send them reeling, inciting them to further flagellations. Sometimes they even seem pleased to do so, grateful for another opportunity to try and make *penance* (that invaluable concept) for their guilt.

That delightful image of a whip lacerating flesh reminds me: above all, you must keep his mind away from those ancient incidents involving a cross and empty tomb. At an unconscious level, make him think that *he* must pay the penalty for his sins. You would think it difficult to tempt a Christian, a *real* Christian, to do this, but they seem to forget the details surrounding their own conversion rather quickly and fail to consider those "incidents" in light of their past, present and future. If he does think about those ancient episodes (you will be able to tell by the calm that will repulsively begin to replace his contorted, guilt-ridden features) immediately divert him back to his own sins. Morbid introspection is one method of inducing this. Sometimes their introspection can be detrimental to us, but excessive introspection can bring in a great yield towards our cause. Foster this through accusations and images surrounding certain sins that have proved difficult for him to let go in the past and believe forgiven. Let him brood over the damage done by his actions as well as imagine in *detail*—remember your training— any possible damaging effects his sin may cause others in the future. Obviously, it would be wise to discourage this kind of thinking if the animal is trying to reinforce himself against a temptation, but once a sin is repented of, this technique is highly beneficial towards rendering him fruitless in the Christian life.

Sincerely,

Senivilous

Letter #2

Dear Gorpussel,

You noted in your last letter that your subject has become somewhat "lazy and indulgent," which is good; I see you are making progress in your attacks. Laziness and apathy with their physical, mental and spiritual torpor hold great benefit, but at this point you need to consider how to weaken your subject if he snaps out of his delirium. It is often temporary, I'm afraid, with these less mature Christians. *He* usually does not allow them to stay in this state for too long. I'm sure by now you've experienced, to some degree, that cruel and strange phenomenon where all your temptations are mysteriously blocked and the animal is somehow given clarity regarding dangers you've led him into. If your subject emerges from the suffocating cocoon of guilt and sin and lethargy you've wrapped him in, he will possibly, with his newfound awareness, move into a season of diligence. If this occurs, propel him into excessive *busyness* rather than diligence. This would be a wise counterattack to heaven's counterattack. Any work empowered by Him is, as you already know, extremely detrimental to our cause, therefore you must confuse your subject, encouraging him to trust himself, to rely on his own powers (our basic strategy for any temptation) to perform various activities. This is the kind of "diligence" to establish.

The approach you should take in tempting him will depend on what direction he expends himself. There are several options he may take in channeling his energies, including the following: he may begin to work harder at the office. Not necessarily a bad thing in and of itself, therefore you must pervert it. See to it that he neglects his relations and other responsibilities at church and home under the guise of "seeking to make the best use of his time" or some other conscience deadening, self-serving lie that makes him feel positively good about his sin. Make him think he is working for others when deep down he knows he is simply indulging himself. A minute's worth of serious scrutiny would reveal this for his real motivation, but he must not think about it. Due in part to our work, many a man, desperate to avoid difficulties associated with taking care of elderly parents or helping their wives with the children, could be found late at the office, starting new projects early, poring over current ones completed or enraptured by some technological diversion.

His shift into action may also take on the form of play in the mode of sports. This is, of course, intrinsically harmless, but holds great potential for distortion in support of our noble vision. Encourage him to become a *connoisseur* of his favorite sport, an expert in the necessary equipment, proper form for the strokes and use of the jargon and so on. It would also be wise to encourage him to study the history and statistics surrounding living and dead luminaries in the field. Teach him to relish his increasing knowledge and growing skill in play (that is, knowledge and skill over others), until, in time, it comes to replace important duties and relationships. This is best done gradually. Use his vanity; provoke excessive competition to bring him, inevitably, into the religious phase of this activity. As you are well aware, there is a nice company of souls confined down here who when living on earth were passionate about sports and their favorite teams to the point of participating in the events, seeking friends with a similar obsession, purchasing expensive merchandise, displaying the colors of their teams, talking and thinking about the players, roaring with delight at their victories, becoming sad at their defeats, yet exhibiting no enthusiasm, possessing no passion for the things of Him. This is the end you should be aiming for.

Another option his transition into diligence may take is in the form of church activities, whether prayer or evangelism or some other nauseating discipline. This is potentially dangerous, but there are distinct methods for neutralizing and distorting this direction as well. I'm sure you remember the maxim in your training: If you cannot corrupt the practice, pervert the motivation. Well, I would add to that by saying that the perversion of *both* is always best, but in this case focus on the motivation of your subject. Foster a slowly ascending pride through excessive involvement. While neglecting others in his family, make him innocently wonder "why other church members are not as involved," that is, as stupendous as him. Work on this nerve until he becomes simply enamored with himself and in his own mind a great saint, a glowing personage before lesser lights. Also, encourage him to increasingly boast about (though sounding humble) his church activities and perform them before the gaze of others. If he ever thinks that he is becoming too concerned with appearances, exploit the tendency of the animals, especially when engaged in church duties, to justify themselves by suggesting he is graciously doing these things to offer *others* (that is, lesser Christians) testimonies and a model of imitation to further the Christian cause.

Sincerely,

Senivilous

Letter #3

Dear Gorpussel,

In your attempt to produce discontentment in your subject, the reason why you have experienced limited success involves your fixation on certain particulars. Using specific disappointments, such as a problem at the office, roof in need of repair, season of illness, or other frustration, is necessary in the early stages, but should only be seen as a means towards producing a more pervasive and permanent mood of discontentment. Staying within your current strategy will only yield a temporary and superficial effect for when the frustration passes so does the desired state of mind. At this point, it would be wise to use the impetus you've gained to darken his mind further, leading him into a mindset that lacks contentment in not only real and *illusory* difficulties, but even in advantages, conveniences and comforts. This is the second step in the process.

In order to push your subject into this next phase, begin to accelerate your attacks in the area of consumption. Start, if he's not enslaved already, into seeing little wants as needs; this will prepare him to view larger desires as absolute necessities. The media in his culture has already primed him towards this. Encourage him to want more and more; establish the virtue of this great dynamic of devouring, first revealed to us by our Master below, in the man's soul. Work on him by suggesting comparisons to other Christians. Use the well-worn, field-tested classic *"if only"* phrases in your temptations. You know, "if only I had a wife" or "if only I had a job I liked" or "more money" or "was more talented" and so on and so on. The list is endless. What you emphasize will, in general, depend on his tastes, gifts, and desires. I know this season can be monotonous and dull, but it is invaluable for leading him more deeply into discontentment and other associated vice such as self-pity.

After working on him for a while at the second level (it may take years to lay this crucial foundation), begin to move him into the third phase by implanting more *general* statements in his thoughts than the previous complaints, things relating to his life as a whole such as: "things *never* work out for me" or "I'll never be happy" and other similar phrases. This will engender an even deeper narcissistic and subjective mindset to the point that his discontentment begins extending out into the nature of the universe, seeing it as dark and against him. Make him think he is being *realistic*, that word which, rather than encompassing the reality of the spiritual world, often holds a wonderfully modern, negative, and materialistic connotation.

Encourage yourself Gorpussel with this thought, that the fourth and final phase, if you reach it, is the most entertaining in the process. Granted, it is difficult to achieve, but here you will start to see the seeds of your work maturate, your eyes beholding the beauty of deeply embedded sins flowering into lush abundance. These bastions of weeds function as our substitute for the repugnant, foul-smelling gardens planted by *Him* in the souls of the saints. I'm afraid these repulsive gardens of holiness exist in every Christian, and some are wider, thicker, and reek more than others, but there are consolations, for all of these gardens contain richly fragrant weeds growing amidst the flowers. It is our duty to sow as deep and wide a crop of them as possible, but I've digressed.

Since the man is a true Christian and, I'm afraid, will always remain one, certain hopes and future glories may still have a foothold in him and therefore he will be, even at this fourth stage, somewhat resistant to atheism, skepticism, cynicism, nihilism or any other beneficial views of that sort. The good news is that he will be *practically* living like a devoted adherent to any one (or combination) of these viewpoints. Your approach will now involve simply preventing him from coming into any kind of vital contact with *Him*, whether encountering Him directly through worship and prayer, or indirectly as He moves through other Christians, the natural world, that barbaric rite involving bread and wine or certain books and especially *that Book*. You will need to be vigilant in placing hindrances and blockades, but really, at this stage, you will find your subject looking for temptations and embracing them with careless unconcern. His discontentment will have reached a terminal, malignant mood which sees almost everything in a negative light. He will be able to look at a sunset or consume a delicious meal and grumble and complain about something in it that was not, but should have been, tailored to his exact specifications. He will be given almost wholly over to fantasies, living a life in his imagination, placing himself or, more specifically, his *feelings*, at the center of the universe, and there he will lie like a spider in the middle of a web, sensitive to the slightest agitation, ready to scuttle across the lines of his phantasmal world to either devour in anger or disappear in fear. His main preoccupation will involve cherishing, protecting, worshipping and preserving the idol of himself, causing his soul to become more and more like the comfortable, flattering, cold and dead fantasy, the demanding phantasm he has surrendered himself to.

Sincerely,

Senivilous

Letter #4

Dear Gorpussel,

My careless mistake of mentioning in my last letter that once the animals become Christians they will always remain so must be seen as a slip on my part. Yes, I do recall now that this discouraging doctrine was banned by the infernal Fathers, including by the revered Barblefap, centuries ago. Thank you for revealing my mistake. I'm grateful for it. Really, sincerely, as well as grateful for the opportunity to train you in our noble work and report with scrupulous objectivity and fairness to our superiors regarding your development. I do hope that my little error does not get out just as I hope that a mistake does not occur in my reports concerning your work, but it can happen so easily. We are all prone to accidents involving damaging omissions, additions and distortions are we not? *Of course* the Christians can lose what they've been given and it is our task to try and bring it to pass. One of the most effective ways to achieve this or, at the very least, render them useless, is through a specific and consistent campaign of doubt.

In using this weapon, your main plan of attack will be in the area of his status as a Christian. You must get him to believe he has been abandoned and forsaken. Once he doubts that pivotal relationship he will doubt all others and the ground once firm to walk on will shake and give way beneath him. When a strong citadel of doubt is erected in his soul, his eyes once slavishly directed towards Him and, as a corollary, humans in need of assistance, will be placed where they should be, on himself. From there it is not too difficult to imagine the kinds of delicious havoc we could render, including, once in a while, the delicacy of a suicide.

Now to your execution of this plan; first off, it is good strategy to prepare your subject for doubt by training him first in becoming an *emotional* Christian. By this, I do not mean that powerful minority of Christians who, empowered and controlled by Him, reveal their passion and adoration for Him in an effusive way before the church and watching world. These types are extremely destructive to our cause. Rather, what I'm referring to are those who believe the presence of Him and His favor is to be gauged solely by a prickling of hairs on the forearms and surge of excitement and, likewise, His distance and disfavor by an absence of these kinds of sensations. A soul like this is extremely fertile ground for planting deep doubt that smothers faith.

Preparing a Christian to be emotional in this way depends, in part, if his personality and experiences incline him in this direction. For a more non-emotional, logical, analytical person, your strategy would have involved tempting him towards rationalism, but since your subject falls in the other general category your approach will be different. First of all, make sure the Christians he associates with are of the same type. This is important; he must not learn from others with different temperaments lest he gain a dangerous and mature balance between reason and emotion. Keep these other types away by tempting him to think they are strange, weird, rude, and so on. When formulating his criticisms, he should either ignore or distort the natural differences in personality and background these others possess. In relation to this, your routine methods for fostering gossip, racism and slander should be useful here. Encouraging him to gorge on electronic media is another way to produce unthinking responses to stimulus. Also, continue to keep him far away from reading, healthy leisure, and reflection; he must consider these activities boring and those who engage in them slothful, while at the same time, always associating crowds, busyness and flashing lights as supremely exciting. There are other methods for making your man thoughtless and overly emotional, but at this point, a few words on the positive application of doubt.

One of the best techniques, a standard approach, involves inciting him to obsess over various pains plaguing mankind around the world along with applying accusations surrounding past sins in his life. You must constantly remind him of illusory sins as well as real sins repented of and the great harm he has done to others and himself and that he is, consequently, beyond the reach of grace. Parade through his mind all sorts of questions and answers that lead to doubt and despair concerning His presence, care, and concern for him (and others). Some of the Christians are receptive towards believing they have committed the unpardonable sin and, thus, without hope. If he is one of these, it is a worthwhile tack to pursue. Above all, distract him from his prayers, isolate him from Christian fellowship and keep him out of *that Book*. And if he does read it, darken his mind; make him read everything in light of how it affects him and his situation even if the verses at hand have nothing to do with it. By this useful method, you can actually get him to make all kinds of reckless applications and see all kinds of fanciful things (including fruitful heresies and passages that seem to condemn him) among the pages that were never intended. This is the kind of interpretation method we've been pushing and tickling the animals with for quite some time now. You would be wise to do the same.

Sincerely,

Senivilous

Letter #5

Dear Gorpussel,

So you have managed to tempt your subject into a state of worry. I imagine you enjoyed watching the effects of your work. How did it manifest itself? Was there a pacing and fretting about, a wringing of hands coupled with sleepless nights? This is well and good but remember this is only temporary; much more work needs to be done. Rather than rejoice now at your brief success, do so later when his soul is secure down here. The following are a few points to follow in preserving this state of mind in your subject for as long as possible and, hopefully, lodging it forever within the man's will.

You should make sure he avoids considering or, at the very least, seriously questioning the sin of worry. It should not be too difficult since this is one of those sins the animals rarely examine with any real depth. They use the word "worrying" regularly, but usually in a manner that trivializes it. In an attempt, whether consciously or unconsciously, to eradicate the guilt they feel at committing this sin, we find it is more common for Christians to talk superficially about it than truly confess and repent of it. A delightful method they often employ when dealing with guilt from other sins as well. If you ever sense your subject starting to analyze this sin with some measure of seriousness, either divert him into thinking about a topic he relishes or diminish his scrutiny by making him think he really isn't worrying (or worrying that much), but merely concerned about the future. You might even be able to convince him that he is simply planning for any forthcoming contingencies. What he must never realize is the fact that worrying, far from being a trifle, centers his affections and trust on himself rather than *Him*.

He must also never realize the utter folly in worrying about the future. Here we have a man, a finite creature who is not only time-bound and spatially limited, but extremely weak and can only control a small amount of circumstances within the tiny portion of the universe he finds himself in. Even in this situation, he could conceivably die before his minor orchestrations are achieved, indeed, an infinite number of possible circumstances could overthrow his most brilliant plans. In light of all this, one wonders at the continued efforts by the humans to perpetually worry about those things they can barely change, not to mention the vast majority of reality impervious to their manipulations. They might as well weep that the world fails to bend according to their will.

From our perspective in the spiritual realm, their machinations are ludicrous and laughable, but they lack that kind of sight. Use this ignorance to your advantage. This leads to my next point.

Your patient must never come to believe the doctrine that we have been trying hard to obscure (with some success) for centuries concerning the sovereignty of Him. If he acknowledges it and allows it to influence his thoughts and actions, you might as well give up on worry and try a different angle of attack. Actually, a firm belief in this dangerous doctrine prepares him for any of our assaults. Not that He is *actually* sovereign you understand, but just the belief that He really is can forearm your subject. Some rumors may have reached you that He is in control of all things; that nothing can come to pass unless He ordains it. This is pure rubbish. Does it look like the world is under the control of some benevolent Guide? I concede He has some power, we've all experienced that, but mark this, we took control of the world and we mean to keep it. We are the ones in control, certainly not *Him*.

Some final thoughts: Worry is basically a manifestation of fear and fear involves, in part, recognizing the uncontrollable elements in existence, therefore, your main approach will always be to simply encourage your subject to use his own resources to try and control them. If he resists, use the tactics you've learned to consistently force him back into this posture. As always, his sin nature will greatly assist you in advancing our program. With regard to his response to worry, the one thing he *must not do* is pray about it. Prayer, real prayer, is a great enemy to worry and any other sin. A shift from abiding in himself to abiding in Him, resulting in the dispersal of worry and a stream of inexplicable peace, is just one of the common, distressing effects of true and fervent prayer. The same unsettling things occur when they engage in true worship. Great harm has been done to our cause by this simple discipline, this seemingly innocuous exercise! There have been times I've despaired over it, wishing there was never such a thing as prayer, but then I remember there are many on earth who think they are praying and sacrificing to their gods when they are really doing so to us, and I feel encouraged again.

Sincerely,

Senivilous

Letter #6

Dear Gorpussel,

The topic of how to lead your subject into *elitism* is a somewhat difficult one, but you are fortunate to have such a wise and experienced guide such as myself, one who has stood on pinnacles, breathing the rarefied air of the heights, tempting kings and monarchs, leading whole nations into sin. If you had consulted lesser tempters you would have, no doubt, come away perplexed, but as it is, in my greatness, I'm well able to respond to your inquiry. I know my current post seems to dictate against my past, but just a few careless words concerning my superior at that time, minor infractions you understand, brought about my demotion. The sentence was grossly unjust, profoundly disproportionate to the offense, but soon I will be restored and recognized once again, taking my place among the most preeminent tempters of all time.

The sin of elitism, that is, the view that certain individuals or groups due to one or more differences, including physical, economic, cultural, racial, and religious differences are, by nature, *better* than others is something we have been leading the humans to believe for a long time. Of course, they're all worthless vermin to us, but it serves our purpose to encourage them to perpetually make distinctions among themselves to determine levels of worth. The manifold benefits of this include genocide, oppression, racism, jealousy, anger, hatred, envy, and a wonderfully deep-rooted and aggressive shade of pride. Other delightful by-products could be mentioned, but this partial list should be enough to reveal the great potential elitism (allied to other sins) holds to help bring about the necessary atmosphere of chaos, division, destruction and pandemonium conducive towards our full habitation and rule.

The basic strategy, whether you are dealing with a Christian or a non-Christian, involves inciting comparison and competition among them as a means to formulate worth. It starts when they are young. We teach them, through their parents and friends, to associate worth based on appearance, behavior, and achievements and from there the list grows. You see, if they can believe one or more of these glaring foundational lies, they will be more inclined to build on it by believing others of a similar kind. These are often the entry points for not only the entrenchment of elitism, which encourages the elitists to act in a predatory manner, but also, on the other hand, for the denigrated to believe themselves utterly worthless, irredeemable, encouraging them to act like prey. Tempting the humans towards one mindset or the other really depends on a number of factors, including personality, gender, upbringing, talents and experiences.

With regard to your subject, he is not quite bright enough for intellectual pride, it would take too much to keep the illusion going, nor does he have a suitable occupation to really push pride in position too far, but there are other angles to choose from. Taking into consideration certain factors such as his age, upbringing, personality and the current cultural climate he finds himself in, you might want to try the elitism through social and economic status approach coupled with pride in appearance and possessions. Make him feel that the inherited status, material means and good looks from his family are due to something inherently meritorious in his relations, even virtuous, a quality (or qualities) that he has, through some mysterious transference, acquired. You'll notice the obvious intellectual difficulty in actually believing this, but no matter, he wants to believe it and you will keep pressing it on him until he does. By this simple, charming method we have seen many souls tricked into committing not only particular sins of elitism, but also whole lives dominated, patterned by it. What he *must not* believe is that anything apart from damnation is grace; that any good gift, no matter the form, is ultimately from *Him* and he is, merely, what they call, a *steward* of these things. What he *must* believe is that these gifts are *deserved*, the inevitable result

25

of something he did or something praiseworthy within him. This incites not only pride, but from out of that source, the tributary of elitism. You should always make him think that he deserves (and others lacking in his qualities do not) this or that, no matter what it is: redemption, talents, a home, health, his paycheck, car, clothes or a meal; never allow him to think these things are gifts bestowed from above. That's the basic rule. Elitism with its attendant sins and miseries will naturally follow.

As previously stated, fostering this sin will help lead to one of our broader goals of bringing whole societies under a more lawless, perverse, corrupt and vicious mode, a more infernal *style*. The glorious riot of this dissonance will be in direct opposition to the nauseating harmony, structure and order that comes about when the animals obey Him rather than us. The idealistic tripe of His view can be found propagated in *that Book* about the animals being created and made in the image of Him and about roles and rules and governing authorities and marriage and sacrifice and submission and all that. In short, our view is realistic; His view is sickening, weak and pathetic.

Sincerely,

Senivilous

Letter #7

Dear Gorpussel,

You raise an important question. How should we, in the most efficient and effective manner possible, provoke the beauties of heresy? Our job has certainly been easier in this century and the last than previous ones. In the past, almost all of the animals held certain basic presuppositions regarding the objective nature of truth. Also, there was less apathy, less indifference once a truth was embraced. They tended to adjust their lives in accordance with what they believed. Now, thanks in part to a long line of certain philosophers (informed by us), most of the animals do not even believe in the universality of truth and if they do, rarely act on it. This has led to a delightful duplicity; theoretically they reject objective truth, but practically speaking live in a manner which continually betrays their belief in it. With regard to sin, particularly sexual, they are impassioned relativists, but with things like the law of gravity and lights governing traffic, committed objectivists. And this has even affected the Christians. In the past, certain doctrines were assumed and expressed by them, but now we find ourselves tempting in an atmosphere where such basic doctrines as eternal punishment and the authority of *that Book* are not universally accepted anymore and, in many quarters, if accepted, never expressed. All this makes the sowing of heresy that much easier. To some degree, a kind of doctrinal vacuum has been created and they have to fill it up with something. We graciously offer them that *something*. The following is a standard approach for teaching our doctrines.

Recognizing that most, if not all of the heresies the animals embrace, can be traced to a defective view of *Him*, we must continually focus our attack on His nature, attributes, and character as expressed in that Book. One of the best approaches towards leading them into heresy involves provoking them to emphasize some attribute (or attributes) of Him to the neglect, denial or suppression of others. In most cases, it means encouraging them to project the dominant proclivity in their personalities unto Him and seeing this as the primary representation of His character. For example, stressing His love at the expense of His wrath, His kindness at the expense of His holiness or His wrath and holiness at the expense of His love and kindness and so on. There are many fruitful possibilities. The importance of this technique cannot be understated since each one of His attributes deepens and augments the others contained within the fullness of Him.

Therefore, any distortion, even a small one, is of value to us.

You might want to encourage your subject to see Him as either immanent without much transcendence or transcendent without much immanence. The former will possibly yield antinomianism and the latter legalism. Since your man is of the more emotional variety, it would probably be best to tempt him towards emphasizing the immanence of Him to the neglect of His transcendence rather than vice versa. The church he attends and many of the Christian leaders he reads and listens to already do this. Push him in this direction. Make your subject *feel* his way into believing this rather than thinking much about it. In time, you may be able to induce him to see Him, as we have managed to achieve with some of the animals, in a kind of pantheistic sense, as a force to be manipulated, a vague benevolent presence, a mist that makes him feel good.

In relation to leading the Christians into heresy by corrupting their understanding of Him, we have made great strides by encouraging many of their pastors and leaders to shun the "theoretical/abstract" for the "practical/concrete," as if there is some kind of antithesis between the two. You see, what they must never ask is what exactly they mean by these terms. What many of them tend to mean by "theoretical," is doctrine that is very difficult to comprehend and has little to no value in the business of life; and what they tend to mean by "practical," is that which is light, comprehended quickly, and applied easily. What they do not understand, and you are to foster this ignorance, is that the theoretical matters in that Book drive their understanding of the more practical ones. They are inextricably connected. The flowering of the practical is rooted in the theoretical. Therefore, if they abandon theory, that is, the depths of doctrine, they will be more susceptible towards heretical views involving practical application. In short, theory is eminently practical because it offers context and drives the practical and thus, in the long run, ignoring theory is not practical, but *impractical*. Now obviously the capacity given to each of them to comprehend doctrine varies greatly, but the principle of continually lowering their patience, desire, and standards in studying, preaching, meditating, teaching and listening to sound doctrine applies. Through our work, many of them, who should be eating the meat of doctrine by now, drink milk or better yet, imbibe the poison of heresy. In short, many of their leaders use the word "practical" as a pretext for cute, sentimental, light, entertaining sermons that often fail to inform, challenge, rebuke or restore anybody, but only make the congregation laugh and smile and look around at one another with that warm complacent glow. And everybody is pleased, especially us.

Sincerely,

Senivilous

Letter #8

Dear Gorpussel,

I found your last letter disappointing. The casual and cursory manner in which you informed me of your subject's bout with self-pity suggests to me you think it a trifle sin. Have you become infected by human sentiment? Swayed by their sensibilities? It is not a mere trifle you ineffectual fool. There are no small sins, just degrees of seriousness and consequence. Do not underestimate the importance of self-pity. If your subject is in that state, try and keep him in it for as long as possible. Set aside any other angles of attack for a little while; focus on pushing him further down into himself. Self-pity is among the best preparatory techniques I know for leading the animals into further transgression. It yields fertile soil for sowing the weeds of vice which will, in time, devour the flowers of virtue. Through the groundwork laid by self-pity we have led many of them into slavery to other sins, including wrath, envy, gluttony, drunkenness and fornication. Self-pity is not true sorrow; it is not a soft sin; it is not an understandable sadness, nor a gentle acceptance to being wounded, nor is it simply remorse or a justified response to some form of suffering, but rather, a fierce rebellion against *Him*. It fosters a proud insistence in the brutes to set themselves up as the sole arbiters of what is right and wrong and to exact a kind of revenge against anyone who dares question it. Ultimately, this admirable sin is an attempt by them to protest, rebel, and express anger and revenge towards Him for allowing some kind of difficulty in their life. They might not see it this way or consciously express it like this, but it is, at the very least, an unconscious assault against heaven. These descriptions, of course, could be said of every sin, but there are few sins that stir these pathetic creatures to rationalize and justify their behavior in such an imaginative and impassioned way as self-pity. Indeed, within the hierarchy of sin, few hold the power this one does to blur distinctions in their minds and paint the disgusting colors of creation in beautifully insipid and bleak hues of gray. While submerged within self-pity, while shackled within the dark cell of it, your subject will have difficulty discerning between fantasy and reality. Not only that, but self-pity will deaden that noxious phenomenon known as joy; it will deliver us from listening to the acrid noise of laughter (the heavenly kind that is) and render them unwilling and unconcerned with helping others. Needless to say, I prize this vice. I believe its seriousness is not only underestimated by them, but by us.

The following are a couple of the most effective methods for keeping your subject in a state of self-pity and, hopefully, for establishing it as a habit.

This sin, in general, emerges from out of discontentment, which often hinges on a real or illusory injustice or simply some natural tribulation experienced during the course of life in a fallen world (glory to us). I'm sure by now you are well aware regarding what exactly this circumstance is. Keep his mind centered on it and, thus, off of Him and onto himself. This is what self-pity desires, but especially the eyes of *others* to be on him that he may be established as the sole concern despite the fact that he lives in a universe replete with suffering. Remind him often of how difficult his trial is and how little people seem to care and why did this happen and so on. Use all kinds of other similar phrases that keep him going round and round various facets surrounding the point of agony. Tempt him to obsession. Provoke all kinds of questions. Could I have done something different to prevent it? How long will it last? Will I be able to bear up against it? Why did this happen to me? The main approach here is to keep him enfolded within himself and away from Him. Once his eyes continually turn to Him in gratitude and worship, despite the circumstances, our cause is lost. The back of self-pity, or any other sins in his life, will be broken.

Ideally, you should first strive to keep him from acknowledging that he is actively engaged in the sin of self-pity by diverting him towards his suffering or encouraging him to avoid accurately diagnosing the real issue. He should regard it as a form of sorrow or a kind of grief or something like that. If he correctly identifies his behavior as self-pity, confuse him with the usual technique of casting false definitions and spurious labels that distort the truth (modern psychology may be helpful here), but if he does recognize it as real sin—hopefully it will not come to this stage—keep his nose out of that Book! His mind needs to be filled with himself, not verses that take him out of himself. Also, keep him indoors and, preferably, in darkness and gloom, far away from the disgusting atrocities of the natural world which, for some reason, many of the vermin regard as magnificent and radiant rather than grotesque and hideous.

Sincerely,

Senivilous

Letter #9

Dear Gorpussel,

By the unsatisfactory account in your last letter, I think you need to be reminded that our primary goal involves fostering the most serious and greatest amount of sin possible without the humans recognizing it as such, and if they do, encouraging them to justify, suppress, or soften it. This ambition leads straight to our ultimate goal of leading them into damnation, wherein they will be eternally, consciously (*it is* conscious and eternal despite what we have been telling them) tormented. In relation to this, it would benefit our cause to consider ways to discourage real confession and repentance—that dreaded phenomenon that leads so swiftly to vital contact with *Him*. The occurrence of it is, obviously, a major obstacle towards the achievement of our ends and therefore, despite the fact I've touched on this topic here and there in previous letters, demands a separate treatment. For the non-Christian, acknowledgment and repentance of sins along with trusting in *the Son*, yields salvation, and for the Christian, growth in sanctification. The consequences of success or failure are enormous, therefore, we must deal with this phenomenon, as in all our endeavors, in the most shrewd and efficient manner possible. You must destroy or diminish this tendency within your subject with that ruthless austerity, that stark viciousness which should be the mark in the execution of all your duties. And please do remember my young fiend the punishment for failure; the same kind of merciless posture you must exhibit in your work may, if you are unsuccessful, fall on you. With that little spur in mind, here is the approach you should take with your subject.

Since he is, as they all are, naturally inclined towards justifying his sinful actions, even the slightest of sins, your basic procedure will involve encouraging *escapism* (the immoral form of it) to prevent confession and repentance. One wise strategy involves *transferring blame* (that wonderful invention of ours), whether onto an inanimate object, other person or, preferably, Him. One basic principle applies here: Keep the mind of your subject *moving* on the round of possibilities for blame. His inner dialogue, driven by real guilt, should be in perpetual motion. You know the game: If only so and so had done this or if I had been feeling better or the weather hadn't affected me or if this had occurred instead of this and so on and so on. The possibilities are endless and often entertaining. The person should eventually fix on something to blame, but why rush the process? You should find it quite easy to tempt your subject towards this because he *desires* to be tempted in this manner and also because the media in his culture encourages this kind of fast-paced, non-meditative mindset.

If your subject acknowledges having committed a particular sin, you must use a more active rather than passive (as in the previous example), form of escapism. There are few things the animals desire to avoid so much as exposure before peers and Him. Therefore, induce extreme agitation in your subject concerning circumstances surrounding confession and repentance and, if applicable, making apologies and recompense. Engender fear by casting terrifying visions of the future, scenes of mockery, scorn, derision, humiliation, shame, and so on. Some of these visions of the future might actually, to some degree, reflect reality, but the point is *fear*. Thanks to us, mankind is driven by various fears, certainly not by a fear of Him.

Also, shroud and darken his mind from the fact of a day of judgment when all will be exposed (our Master below has assured us that the rumor of *our* judgment is mere propaganda), for belief in such a forthcoming event is never beneficial towards the achievement of our ends. Push procrastination; build up this beneficial habit in him. Make him feel that the present duties are pressing enough and he will get to it, in time, but is currently just too busy. Remember your training. He must feel the tyranny of the temporal, that he has so many *important*—he must not define important in any transcendent kind of manner—things to do. Keep him busy. Not the balanced form of diligence which we despise, but the obsessive, mindless form of it. This is a highly efficient way to encourage an escapist attitude towards dealing with sin. They are always so busy in the contemporary world are they not? This is partly due to the fact that we have duped them into believing that mere busyness is somehow *successful*, even virtuous. If they would examine themselves, they would find that what often drives them is not the desire to embrace reality, but the desire to *avoid* it, especially contact with Him.

If your temptations are effective, your subject, in order to avoid real confession and repentance that He might avoid His Presence, will either plunge into the escape of a frenetic busyness or the murk of a listless torpor. In time, he will become forgetful or cavalier about sin, perhaps even to the point of arriving at the belief that he did no wrong or, better yet, that his actions were somehow ethical.

Sincerely,

Senivilous

Letter #10

Dear Gorpussel,

I knew you were naive, but did you not learn already that you may not possess your subject? I'm afraid controlling him in that manner is quite impossible. We have never been able to possess a true Christian. Somehow *He* prevents it. There are some tempters, even a few high-ranking ones (Vomsteeb is among their number), who think we will eventually be successful in finding a way to do so, but I doubt it. Once He takes a human being captive, He erects a banner in his soul declaring ownership, that is, ownership in a special sense since He *claims* ownership over everything, and all our attempts to maneuver past Him and reclaim our property meet with failure. This is, of course, an outrage, blatant thievery, bad sportsmanship, but this is the kind of behavior we've come to expect from Him. Now we may, depending on how much place the Christians give to us through sin, influence the animals (sometimes greatly), but the kind of mastery and authority over them you are thinking of only occurs among those who are not in His camp, but in ours. Even then, leading non-Christians to become controlled by us to that extent is not common. I do have pleasant memories of possessing several of them during the course of my distinguished career, but also remember on one occasion the pain of being exorcised. It happened almost two thousand years ago. We, for there were many of us, were simply minding our own business, enjoying the possession, especially the sport of making our prey howl day and night among tombs and mountains and cut himself with stones, and then *He* showed up with His band of vagabonds. Well, desperate to avoid the "restlessly passing through waterless places phenomenon," we politely asked for permission to enter into a large herd of pigs feeding on a hillside. Immediately after our request was granted, we found ourselves evicted (from our rightful residence I might add) in a rather brutal fashion. We then entered into our new residency which was not quite as desirable as the previous one. Pigs are somewhat lacking in functionality you understand. After this, we found ourselves suddenly rushing down the hillside and plunging into the sea, where the squealing beasts drowned. You would think He might, after forcibly ejecting us from one house, allow us to stay for a reasonable amount of time in another, but failed in even this small courtesy. As I said before, we've come to expect this kind of behavior from Him.

Now, despite the sad reality, it would be wise to make your subject *think* he can be possessed. It will provoke fear, doubt and insecurity and keep his eyes on himself and us, which is where we want them, rather than fixed on Him. With regard to his knowledge of us, there are other related lies it would be wise to tempt him to adopt in his thinking. The following are a few of them.

I'm sure you've noticed by now that some of the Christians talk and act as if our Master below is omnipresent; sometimes they even talk as if he's omnipotent and omniscient, despite the fact he is a creature and, thus, spatially and chronologically bound, not to mention limited in power and knowledge. If your subject has not embraced these errors in his thinking, it would be wise to try and impress them upon him, but make sure he adopts them somewhat unconsciously lest he become aware of their ridiculous nature. The ideal involves occupying his mind with all kinds of fearsome falsehoods that paralyze yet remain unchallenged, untouched by serious analysis.

Another wise tactic for distorting his thinking, involves inciting him to passively accept the view that we can control and read his mind. As I'm sure you've figured out by now, we cannot, despite our best efforts, control or read their minds, only consider their past responses to temptation, listen to their conversations, observe their actions and facial expressions and from that basis decide on the best kind of temptation to use and angle to send the salvo.

Also, foster the idea in your subject that he is not really responsible for his sins (or at least not for some of them), and effectively eradicating his problem with indwelling sin involves primarily warring against us, rather than applying certain principles found in that infuriating Book for warring against the sin nature. In short, encourage him to enthusiastically fight phantasms, which can lead to disillusionment when the sin-pattern remains, but you must be careful because sometimes we *really are* attacking and tempting him and if he, empowered by Him, fights us, we will have to depart for at least a season or engage in a long firefight. The Christians actually do have great authority in His name to rebuke us and command us to leave, but they must not realize this, believing they have either far more authority than they actually do or too little. If too much, they will, hopefully, exalt themselves and arrogantly demand things from Him as well as enter into arenas of combat against us without adequate preparation. If too little, they open themselves up for attack and like the weak, timid, little things they are, throw down their arms and run at the first scent of battle.

Sincerely,

Senivilous

𝔏etter #11

Dear Gorpussel,

I received with pleasure the latest account of your work. You did well in gradually leading him into jaded acceptance of certain *soft* forms of pornography. Up there, the fools would not even label it as soft pornography since the images were devoid of specific nudity, but we know better. It was wise to tempt him to look at magazines with attractive models selling lingerie and sexy bathing suits and at advertisements and flyers that flaunt the physical to provoke sales, not to mention certain movies, television programs and music videos that purport to be about this and that but are primarily about the scenes containing pretty women exposing themselves. Deep down, this is one of the main reasons, along with the bedazzlement of special effects (and shock of violence), why many men watch television or visit the theater. This does not mean pornography is only imbibed by males either, for the females are becoming increasingly entranced by it as well. The reception of these soft forms of pornography and the more graphic kind in his culture has exceeded even our own expectations. Pornography is now popular, accepted, and this cannot help but get into the mind of your subject, making him think the lesser forms are no big deal since he is not looking at *real* pornography. Of course, his mind is probably a pornographic playground by now, and the images devoured are, no doubt, visited often in his imagination for perverse, vicarious explorations. Despite the likelihood that he now has a harem of voluptuous beauties parading about his mind, it might still be a challenge for you to encourage your subject, since he is a Christian, to look at the more perverse forms of pornography because he definitely knows it is wrong. With the softer variety sometimes you can, to some degree, diminish their sense of it as sin, but with the more graphic imagery this is difficult. Recognizing this challenge, there are a few excellent techniques for leading him into it.

What your subject needs to continue further down this dark, descending path is simply some time sampling the harder stuff. Once this occurs, it will infect him for life and will be extremely difficult to pull away from; he will long to turn back to it and will probably do so again and again despite the fact that its comforts will gradually decrease and constrictions increase. In time, like a drug-addict seeking more potent drugs, he will need more perverse forms to feel the same rush of pleasure. To prep him for this initial encounter, confuse him concerning the great disparity between the ease in acquisition and consumption of pornography and the detrimental, long-term ramifications. In other words, he must think his actions involve only the immediate experience of thrills and excitement without the severity of consequences or, at least, must think the consequences minimal. Prod him into making that fatal decision to experience its pleasures with the usual round of self-satiating lies and fantasies. Pressure from immoral friends has also proven particularly beneficial with this sin.

Among helpful preparatory states, such as loneliness, laziness, self-pity, discontentment and envy to induce before tempting your subject into this sin, anger is also worth mentioning. We've ensnared many a Christian man into pornography because they were simply angry, whether consciously or unconsciously, about something, sometimes what they perceive as a failure by *Him* to bring them a spouse according to their specific timetable or something of that sort. Knowing this, it would be wise to send forth the fiery darts of anger to prepare him for the assault of lust.

If a human you are working on has already been exposed to the more graphic form of pornography it will make your work much easier; in this situation you should use one of our greatest lies, the "well it's too late now might as well continue looking" line. We've also used this kind of lie with great effectiveness with those who have lost their virginity. It's the fatalistic "it's too late now" kind of temptation as if after the initial sin they might as well develop a pattern of sinful behavior. The strangeness and beauty of this temptation is that it often works!

Keep vigilant. Focus on your task; if your attack proves successful, the pornographic habit will yield spectacular results, leading him into other sins. What enters through his eyes will get into his heart, making him unfit for the kind of commitment necessary for marriage and other relationships. The pliable, gorgeous, willing, flexible, unapproachable fantasies gorged on in his imagination will make him increasingly unable to relate to a real woman. In his mind, the females of his race will change from human beings possessing a soul into purely physical contrivances whose value will be based solely on their capacity to excite, that is, how closely they resemble his stunning fantasies, and impart pleasure to your subject. I could go on with the benefits, the divorces, adulteries, fornications, sexual molestations, rapes, murders (particularly of the unborn), slavery, and depression and other miseries this sin helps to engender, but it should suffice to say that the carnage is delicious and incalculable.

Sincerely,

Senivilous

Letter #12

Dear Gorpussel,

Your comments and questions concerning the topic of anger reveal that you are putting on some diabolical muscle, but you still have much to learn. You were partly correct in a couple of points regarding the nature of unrighteous anger, but in the area of practical application, your technique could use some more extensive refining. Having said that, anger is a more ferocious sin against Him than you detailed; the following are a few comments towards a more precise understanding of certain theoretical aspects regarding the nature of sin.

Some sins (in thought, word, or deed) are consciously committed, others unconsciously; some involve the failure to act, and others are more forceful. Ultimately, each sin, including unrighteous anger, is an attempt, whether consciously or unconsciously, to reduce the glory of, diminish, accuse, defame, or even annihilate, *Him*. When sinning, every single one of them, even the Christians, at least for the duration of the particular sin, tries, at some level, to do this. And these sins will always involve idolatry, and these mutable idols will always betray them. The main idol will always be that of the *self*, which involves one worshiping (through various means) oneself and often the attempt to direct the worship of others towards oneself. There may be secondary idols associated with this, but the self is the core idol. Furthermore, there is always a level of escapism or *unrighteous fantasy* in sin, which involves *suppressing the truth* in an attempt to hide from the presence of Him, justify sinful desires and actions—in part to retain their pleasures—and avoid the terror of judgment. Whenever we successfully tempt one of the humans to sin, we are encouraging a radically rebellious and treasonous attempt by him to usurp the authority of, and exalt himself over, the so-called *Creator* (to use that presumptuous and overstated title). This is, in essence, the delightfully corrupt and beautifully arrogant base from out of which every single sin emerges.

Now on to the more practical side of things, with regard to your subject, rather than solely tempting him towards wrath by provoking him to repeatedly replay the offensive words spoken against him by his friend, you must tempt him to think irrationally about the possible insult and the manner in which it was rendered. Your subject's friend was either offering some helpful criticism or spoke something truly offensive. If the comment was actually constructive it must not be seen as such. Instead, it must be regarded as a profoundly vicious insult of a high order. Once you successfully tempt him to believe the false and highly speculative assumption that his friend intended to speak ill of him, move him onto the conviction that he is now a deliberate enemy. This is best done by furthering an unrealistic assessment of the situation; play on the memory of the comment, making sure he misinterprets it. Stress certain gestures and facial expressions of his friend and specific words as full of hostile meaning. Encourage your wounded subject to not only retain, but relish and nurse vindictive, spiteful, and resentful feelings towards him. In his suspicious, mindless state of anger, you may even manage to get your subject to believe other preposterous things such as the notion that his friend is a ringleader and there are others involved in a kind of whispering conspiracy against him. Tempting him in this direction depends, in part, on his past and how sensitive, imaginative, mentally and emotionally weak he is. The exercise of inflaming deep, internal hatred and, hopefully, open wrath can be enjoyable, but do not forget your business. You must be careful, consistent, and deliberate in your application, remembering to avoid pushing him too far lest he waken to the realization that he is acting remarkably irrational.

If the comment by his friend was indeed an insult, your task will be that much easier. In this circumstance, as in the previous one, tempt him to *react* rather than truly *think* about the situation. Objectivity, proportion, and a healthy sense of context along with a sense of placing the insult within a system of degrees, a hierarchy of severity, must melt before his scorching anger. His unthinking state will promote antipathy rather than empathy, causing him to lose perspective by disregarding his friend's personality and past difficulties as well as the possibility that he may have simply been having a bad day or spoke offensively as a result of misconstruing something done or said. The immature comment must warrant a series of immature, vengeful, retaliatory responses back. Not that a verbal response is always the best course to tempt him towards, sometimes it is more beneficial to work on the fear of man angle, inciting him to harbor the anger, causing it to fester and, if all goes well, degenerate into bitterness which cannot help but spread its sweet corruption internally as well as externally in the lives around him. Most importantly, the kind of weak, effeminate and pathetic counsel offered in *that Book* about reconciliation and answering gently, and taking things patiently, forgiving from the heart, looking at oneself first to root out hypocrisy, and confronting a brother in humility and love rather than remaining indignant, furious and slanderous, should all be blindly ignored by him as befits one we've trained well in the infernal disciplines.

Sincerely,

Senivilous

Letter #13

Dear Gorpussel,

Your questions concerning how to tempt your subject to misuse money, whether as a reckless spender or miser, touch mainly on external manifestations rather than the internal corruption—the obsession with money, the love of it—you should seek to establish. It's not of course the love of the physical money itself, the printed paper that people are concerned with, but what it can acquire for them, including material possessions as well as, to some degree, a form of security, freedom, power and control. There is also the pleasure to be obtained at simply *having*, that is, having more than others and making sure they know it. In its more insatiable form, avarice involves the passion to acquire regardless of the harm it may cause to others and oneself. Through this sin we have led many into financial, physical, mental, emotional and, best of all, spiritual ruin. The success of our work can be seen all over the earth. The miseries perpetuated by greed have been endless. See the middle-aged man who disregards himself, his family and, of course, *Him* in his heedless pursuit of wealth. There he is, compulsively gathering more and more until one day a major financial calamity befalls him and he feels his life, his identity, gone, and encouraged by us, calmly, deliberately, places the end of a pistol-barrel to his temple and to our great delight pulls the trigger. See the young woman who in her lust for ease prostitutes herself by marrying a man she neither loves nor admires but is able to provide her the kind of lavish comfort, security and material things she desires. Now see her as an older woman who has gone through two divorces and finds herself lonely, troubled and confused, yet still trying to load her pockets with gold, her mind disintegrating amidst her desperate search for more. But the greatest expression of our success can be seen down here in these lightless pits, this gloomy abyss, where a number of greed-contorted souls reside and who, in their unbridled lust, amassed much on earth, but now count among their intense agonies the *loss* of everything for all eternity. Thousands and thousands more of these kinds of stirring testimonies could be told and many more will follow in the future. It is the legacy of the virtue of greed and *we* are the architects of it. Let us do hope for your sake that you to will be able to offer a testimony of success regarding your subject. Consider the following stratagems.

Enchant his eyes with those who flaunt their wealth; tempt him to covet their glories and see great wealth as a means to overcome his insecurity and sense of being a failure. Make him jealous, envious of the successes of others. Throw enticements into his mind about the great attractiveness he will acquire with women if he manages to make more money. I'm well aware that your subject is already moderately wealthy, but this never stops the greedy. They always want more. Remember my letter on discontentment when working your temptations. As usual, his sin nature will greatly assist you. Also, make him feel (whether it's true or not) he has little to no respect or honor (as defined in the worldly sense) among his friends, family and neighbors and that a more beautiful home and car etc. will convince them to change their attitude towards him. Work on this nerve until he becomes positively ravenous at the prospect of proving to them he is worthy of respect and honor. Cast visions in his brain of future vindications. Obviously, the dominant theme here, as it is with every sin, is the virtue of pride, or extreme self-absorption and self-exaltation.

You may ask if it is possible to push a Christian this far into what should be an obvious sin. In my experience it depends on the kind of animal you're striving to manipulate. I've encountered Christians who were quite accommodating towards my ideas and others rather inflexible. The resistant ones merely require more subtlety. Each has their peculiar weaknesses; you must simply find and exploit them. Your subject is a decent candidate for greed and probably does not require too much cunning for you to achieve victory in this area, but it will take time. Be encouraged, on your side are a couple of popular preachers he likes, each persuasively teaching their own alluring brand of worldliness, leading many to be discontent, demanding, and greedy.

Finally, strive to exclude from his thinking the idea of heaven since it will tend to have the negative effect of encouraging him amidst trials and steeling him against avarice or any other temptation. If you fail in this, make heaven vague, abstract, indistinct and boring in his consciousness. Despite the fullness of its solid, faultless, vivid actuality (how I hate the memory of it!), render it like a kind of amorphous dream in his mind and since that will fail to excite or inform, it will also fail to influence. One day we will storm heaven and transform it into a land of dark, discordant bedlam, but currently, for some reason, we have not yet been able to penetrate its blinding incandescence and the paralyzing purity of its air.

Sincerely,

Senivilous

Letter #14

Dear Gorpussel,

Amidst the rubbish of your report, there was one portion of interest: the digression concerning the atmosphere of your subject's church. Through your account, as well as dialogue with the tempter in charge of corrupting that particular congregation, I've gathered certain attitudes within it that your subject should be encouraged to adopt and others persuaded to reject. First, the concept of *atmosphere*. It could be defined as basically the presence of spiritual realities and, sometimes, physical elements (and any combinations thereof) in any given place. A great deal can be conveyed, directly and indirectly, through atmosphere, and its immense potential as a tool for our cause should not be ignored. It can draw the humans to inexorably embrace, sometimes unconsciously, a certain mood along with the beliefs suffused within it. Different atmospheres, whether glaring and obvious or vague and mysterious, populous or not, hold varying levels of influence, whether for good or evil, though often it's a mixture of both, with one predominant. When the atmosphere is primarily in our favor, tempt your subject to mindlessly, emotionally embrace it and suppress, ignore or dismiss any concerns for the sake of peace. Play on the desire they all have to conform to the majority. If the atmosphere is primarily opposed to our cause, tempt him to become a critic, concerned solely with perceiving its vices to the neglect and, if you play him well, denigration of any virtues.

There are several aspects in his church supportive of our efforts, but along with this, there are also, I'm afraid, a number of aspects diametrically opposed to our cause. The following are a couple of things your subject should disregard. First, he should strive to avoid that repellent old woman that you mentioned in your last letter. I've encountered her on other fronts. She is a very advanced soldier in His army. The noxious pest has been a nuisance for years with her constant humble prayers, fierce devotion and obedience to Him. We have tried to render her inoperable but have failed and every attempt to make her ineffective has also been a failure or met with only brief, limited, unremarkable success. If your subject gets near her, he will sense His Presence through her in a powerful way and will be affected, encouraging him to put away sin and live more passionately for Him. Tempt him to evade and dismiss her by making him think she's fanatical and extreme or trying to draw attention to herself.

Also, there is a fairly strong measure of unity and fellowship within the church, including charity over secondary doctrines. This is a problem. One expects resistance in leading them to depart from uniformity on main doctrines—what they regard as the non-negotiable essentials—but not from *charity* over minor doctrines, the non-essentials. Rather than regard conformity to secondary issues as the criterion for orthodoxy they simply *lovingly* and seriously debate them and then laugh when there is no agreement, but there's still some hope. There are usually at least one or two individuals in every church who are divisive over minor doctrines; lead your subject to them. Make sure he becomes excited over their enthusiasm. Encourage these aggressive, schismatic ones to take it upon themselves to befriend and tutor him. In time, a faction may grow and one of our greatest works, that beloved phenomenon, the church-split (over non-essentials), may occur. Often it takes only one prominent member in a church to help bring it about.

Among the aspects within your subject's church that he must embrace, two are especially promising. The first involves an ongoing over-emphasis on sinfulness by the leaders rather than a balance between sainthood and sinfulness. This tends to breed legalism as well as despondent weariness while the other extreme of continually over-stressing sainthood without a corresponding concern over sin, tends to engender antinomianism and mindless exuberance. If we fail to produce an entertainment-centered church and leaders insist on dealing with these two general doctrinal categories, either extreme is worth inducing. Currently, it is not common (thanks to us) to find a church pursuing a balanced fullness where each of these broad concepts coalesce, continually informing the Christian with not only an understanding of his position in Him, but an awareness of his sinfulness and, thus, absolute dependence on Him.

The second promising aspect is the tendency of the congregation to do relatively little with the knowledge they acquire (other churches have zeal without knowledge, but the best are those without knowledge or zeal). They enjoy the preaching and teaching and talk extensively about sin, the lost, and cultural evils, but do little about it. In short, the church is not that dangerous because of the sin of disobedience, but they are starting to sense that they should do more to fulfill that revolting command—what they call *The Great Commission*. Your subject should embrace apathy and resist action. Make him *feel* faithful and obedient to Him because he strives to garner knowledge; encourage a glow of pride at his efforts to acquire it in comparison to the laziness of others. Work him over with these kinds of thoughts until the comfort of complacency, a lavish mood of insulated ease, a voluptuous feeling of indifference, wraps him like a thick warm blanket.

Sincerely,

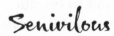

Letter #15

Dear Gorpussel,

In your last letter you mentioned that your subject seems to have entered into a state of apathy. This is good. It's certainly a posture well worth promoting and, in this case, extending. I'm assuming you are not equating apathy with laziness. It is not laziness for apathy can also involve busyness, but simply lacks desire. The sin of apathy involves, to some degree, a lack of hunger, love, feeling, emotion, and concern for *Him* and, consequently, the things of Him. Your subject will respond to this state in basically one of five following ways: First, he might, rather than resist, surrender himself to apathy, resulting in a lack of physical, mental and spiritual activity. Secondly, he might make an aggressive attempt (in his own strength) to revive himself through various activities. The third involves a deliberate evasion of apathy through a descent into various diversions. The fourth involves an *unconscious* attempt to run away from what he senses deep within by plunging into a world of diversions. The fifth response involves confession and repentance

59

and seeking Him anew through the spiritual disciplines. Obviously, we wish to avoid this last possibility. In light of your subject's personality and the fact he seems to be only slightly cognizant of his predicament, tempt him into a variation of the fourth response.

One way to divert him from recognizing and dealing with his apathetic state is to make him think he is simply suffering from fatigue, sickness or stress due to some external cause. Your subject will wonder, at some level, what is happening; make sure he places the problem solely within the physical realm. His inner man should be left unexamined. His gaze should be outside of himself but, of course, not towards *Him*. Since you are working with a Christian rather than a pagan, you might have to dance a finer line with your temptations here. Christians tend to be more rigorous analyzers of their souls but, thankfully, the form of this discipline we despise has eroded some over the last couple of centuries. Since he will be dimly aware of something amiss within, remotely alert to something he just cannot seem to discern, lead him to unwittingly grope towards erroneous solutions. This may actually brighten him up a bit. Direct his gaze towards some hobby or project in the home or yard that he has not quite been able to get to. It will bring him a kind of temporal, superficial relief. If these temptations fail and he insists on inner scrutiny, make sure it is either cursory, casual and sentimental or excessive, indulgent and maniacal.

By the way, it is possible that *He* has withdrawn from your subject the *sense* of His Presence for a season (for the purpose of strengthening him). It can be hard to tell. If so, he might not be guilty of apathy. The withdrawal thesis is doubtful though. It seems more likely your subject is suffering the consequences from habits and patterns of sin we've sown and cultivated within him. This could be the first fruits of that bountiful harvest of sin we've been laboring so hard to produce! Indeed, this is probably what it is. You see, a number of the Christians have, to some degree, given themselves over to apathy. Sometimes even I wonder what they are about. The vibrant ocean of the spiritual world bleeding constantly over the borders into their earthly realm—indeed nature and their own souls reveal something of it—(not to mention that abominable Book), pressing the weight of its reality upon them at every moment, yet still they persist in pursuing the temporal. Thanks be to the fall of man! Because of it (and many of our other magnificent works), they're consumed with desire over that which is vanishing, fleeting and ephemeral. Are they not aware of the vast ramifications of their seemingly small actions and decisions? Do they not realize eternity looms just beyond the swiftly fading vapor of their bodies? Sometimes my young fiend, I simply laugh as I watch them run around pursuing this and that, impassioned over a piece of junk here, worshiping some aspect of creation over there, I just laugh, howling over these dumb little ants building and building monuments to themselves, swarming over dead things, picking at them as if they were the choicest of morsels. The blindness of their indifference to the transcendent, their focus on the transitory, unconcern with immortality, is so heartening at times I can barely contain myself. Well, I see I've digressed, but you can hardly blame me for it.

Final instructions: If he becomes aware of his state of apathy (they often eventually do), lure him into legalism (#2 on the previous list); incite a flesh-driven asceticism to avoid a dreaded confession and repentance fiasco. If he yearns to recover desire, this temptation, which appears and sometimes feels like spiritual desire, will be particularly compelling. If it is a season where He has withdrawn the sense of His Presence from him, you should see it as an opportunity to work him over with doubt, to gnaw away at his faith, implode his sense of hope, and then, at the right time, tempt him into some scandalous sin using his desire to not only *feel* something, anything, but to manipulate, to try and blackmail heaven into a response.

Sincerely,

Senivilous

Letter #16

Dear Gorpussel,

So you wish to be instructed on how to tempt your subject towards legalism. It is one of our prime works in not only keeping souls from being converted since, in essence, legalism is an attempt to work one's way into heaven (one of our greatest lies), but in distracting and rendering innocuous those already within the Christian camp. One of the beauties of this temptation, when successful, is how profoundly deceptive it is. With some sins, the subject knows he is doing something wrong, but with legalism it's not uncommon for him to think he is doing something right. It rates high on the self-deception scale. Since it is so difficult for one committing this sin to see it for what it is, it tends to endure, sometimes for the entire life of those it infects. You'll also find the manifestations of legalism, the hypocrisy, slavery, mindless rituals, irrelevant concerns and blind arrogance over what is minor or worthless highly entertaining.

There are several forms of legalism, including

the invention of a false law by misinterpreting, distorting, taking away or adding to the true law (often making it easier to fulfill). Another form of legalism involves the exaltation of lesser issues over weightier ones. In this approach the legalist follows the true law but fails to make distinctions between what is more or less important and, as a result, tends to become proud by comparing himself to others. There is also the form which prohibits practices where *that Book* has left them free, leading the legalists to reproach or condemn those who fail to conform to the illusory standard. All these forms of legalism involve, at some level, a concern with external appearances to the neglect of internal character. And they all oppose that hideous reality rendered by Him known as *grace*, whether grace that leads unto salvation or, if the man is a Christian, grace that brings further sanctification. I think the best approach for your subject will involve inducing him to exalt his virtues and downplay his weaknesses combined with the fabrication of a false law or two. Consider the following instructions.

With those laws and commands where it is easy for your man to obey, remind him of just how faithful and wonderful he is, leading him to generate a nice little ripple of applause towards himself, an undercurrent of self-satisfaction flowing beneath his thoughts. He should never consciously question this perpetual rhythm of self-congratulation in the back of his mind, but if he does, dismiss it as a trifle, undermining the seriousness of it. From this point, lead him into the delicious, almost harmless little turn where he begins to wonder why certain others have such a difficult time with obedience in the areas he is strong in, marveling that they are not mature like him, but secretly delighting in their shortcomings. These disobedient others should be seen (whether it's true or not) as failing because they do not study as much nor practice the disciplines as faithfully as him etc. At this stage, slowly tempt your subject to regard himself as something quite special, as climbing up towards a lofty pedestal and other souls as specks far below; he should regard them as increasingly inconsequential in comparison to him. Your subject may even suffer from the delusion that *He* is fonder of him than most of His other saints. Make sure you stress the word *others* to your subject, that is, those who are at a distance from his magnificence.

At this point, beyond inciting him to exalt himself for success in areas of obedience to His laws and commands, encourage him to continue his so-called victories by establishing laws birthed out of pure fantasy or borrowed from the opinions of others such as forbidding the playing of cards or dressing casually for church. In his eyes, these fabrications must be obeyed by those who desire to be truly triumphant and obedient saints and those who fail to do so should be regarded as pathetic spiritual weaklings. It may also be beneficial here to push him into false humility to hide the reality of his sin. He should conceal the contempt in his heart towards others, while at the same time referring to them, deceptively, with an appearance of humility, as simply weaker brothers and sisters, or even as stronger Christians than himself. This way he will be using lies and flattery to win approval while furthering his sense of superiority. No doubt, many of them probably are stronger, but he would find this notion absurd. In truth, he holds them in disdain.

You will find legalism has many delightful by-products, including the unique tendency by those under its sorcery to insist that others conform to their legalistic behavior and with the same measure of rigor, surrendering individuality. It resists diversity in personality and diminishes freedom. Where Christians are bound (by *that Book*) it corrupts; where they are free it shackles; when shackled by iniquity it binds more deeply. In short, I love legalism; it's a veritable playground for misery and sin! You will also find your subject exhibiting an uncanny knack at seeing weaknesses and faults in others and then exaggerating them before his eyes because, of course, legalists must have some kind of negative, real or imagined, to help in highlighting what they perceive as their positive qualities.

Sincerely,

Senivilous

Letter #17

Dear Gorpussel,

With regard to your query concerning the kind of spirituality to lead the humans into, there are many possibilities, all fashioned by us. For some of the dupes it's far better to tempt towards materialism, for others a spiritual direction. It depends on their personality and past along with other factors. Generally speaking, for the more logical, practical, business-type of a man, usually the flat, materialistic options work best. For the more sensitive, intuitive, artistic types, the inflated, spiritual options tend to be more effective. The following are a few principles on this topic that may prove beneficial in your overall career as a tempter.

Concerning the many false philosophies, religions, cults, and occult practices we've developed over the centuries, the humans should regard them as liberating, an ascent into the light of unfettered freedom, and Christianity, invented by *Him*, as enslaving, a descent into the dark of an ancient dungeon. As a matter of fact, it would be highly beneficial for them to think of the options we've designed as having been denigrated, stifled, and suppressed by the Christian church for underlying motives centering on money, power and control over the masses. With respect to any examples in history when this was actually the case, bring it to their attention with glaring and graphic immediacy. They must think the motivations of Christians have always been and always will be to oppress and deceive for personal gain. This will be very appealing, making them feel *enlightened* by our views and empowered to become freedom fighters on a mission to expose the lies of the church and warn others. And, of course, where history is opposed to our perspective, they must interpret it in a biased, subjective manner, revising it accordingly, driven in part by their desire to eradicate Christianity and, thus, restraints on their sinful behavior. This behavior, in particular, often involves sexual immorality and, in general, the process of training, muffling, and hardening (when it's operating against us) the conscience. With regard to this moral law within, by the way, you may need to tempt them to redefine it according to modern standards. They should see it as something arbitrarily constructed or manufactured by man rather than designed and implanted by Him. Tempt them to believe it was derived from blind chance or conventions, traditions, social customs, inherited beliefs or something else. This will, to some degree, smother their feelings of guilt and shame but may fail to fully harden the biting clench of the conscience—that incessant moral chatterbox—hopefully pushing them into more forceful attempts at silencing its foolishness.

Cutting the fabric of our philosophy into cloaks that appear glittering and gorgeous to appeal to different kinds of people (who engage in different kinds of pursuits) takes skill and persistence. Our program requires a diversity of applications with all appearing good—ways leading into freedom and perfection—while really leading into oppression and destruction. For example, some materialists embrace communism, others humanism. For those inclined towards a combination of spirituality and materialism, sometimes we pose as aliens, telling them we are highly evolved superhuman beings with extraordinary powers, that we reign like gods and we've guided them at points throughout history and soon, if they just follow our guidance, they will evolve into what we have become and so on. Lies, such as one of our greatest, the myth of evolutionary theory, breeds more of the same. They build on each other, rising into grand, sparkling edifices of sand. For other groups we mask ourselves as phantoms, as spirits of the dead, fashioning the alluring deception of a counterfeit heaven—an everlasting existence of bliss—with death the only demand for entrance. For feminists we teach them to awaken the goddess within, which is part of that radical ecology movement we've concocted with its various views, including pantheism and animism, spirits in trees and flowers and all that rubbish. Even polytheism, due, in part, to certain cults, is on the rise. Indeed, all of our inventions (with certain exceptions) are increasing, each promising their own brand of ascension, while, amusingly, betraying into the abyss. And the masquerade continues with so many of them willing to dance, whirling to our lead. Soon enough we will remove the dazzling beauty of our masks to their astonishment and horror and our laughter. Indeed, they will all, one day, have their own masks stripped away.

With regard to all of these worldviews we are promulgating, it is imperative that they misinterpret, deny, drown out or ignore that insistent voice of reality that often frustrates our efforts, whether they hear Him speak directly, or indirectly through creation, history, sermons, their conscience or *that Book*. That is, they must allow the desires of the world, their sin nature, and us to inform them regarding what is truth, even if that means believing the *truth* of the denial of truth. That reminds me; they should also resist Him speaking indirectly through logic lest they uncover some of the many ridiculous contradictions we breed in their thinking. If we fail at this, tempt them to regard the acceptance of contradictions as the very essence of wisdom. Perversion should be their creed and irrationality their religion.

Sincerely,

Senivilous

Letter #18

Dear Gorpussel,

Taking into consideration your reports as a whole, I've noticed many glaring errors, including the following defect. You have an inadequate knowledge of the nature of the kind of creature you are tempting. It would, of course, be obvious to say your knowledge of his motivations, intentions and attitudes (among other related aspects) is deficient, but I mean his actual physical and spiritual make-up, the stuff of him. This basic knowledge is required before you can comprehend more deeply the inner world of these strange mortals. Knowing your prey better will make you a more effective hunter. This is crucial, but so often neglected by you junior tempters. In your last report, the casual statement about your subject's trichotomous nature served to reveal, yet again, your ignorance. Mankind is dichotomous in nature. They are a revolting hybrid of soul and body and these two components affect each other. Both aspects in the animals, the spiritual and grubby component of their physicality are

71

mysteriously united; they interact, complement and influence each other, yet, in some sense, remain distinct. I know this is repugnant, but there you have it. They are truly bizarre, nasty creatures, unworthy of our attention; why we condescend to even tempt and destroy them has been a perennial question, but always we're forced to recognize their necessity in our plan of rebellion. And besides, there are pleasures associated with bringing about their ruin, especially the sweetness of revenge by debasing His image in them. I wish we could deface every reminder of Him. Unfortunately, His fingerprint is found all over creation. Our Master below, not Him, should be the one propagating his image throughout heaven and earth! Returning to our main discussion; do remember that it would be wise for you to encourage the trichotomous heresy among the Christians; it can lead them into certain other errors that work to our advantage.

With regard to non-Christians, one of the strongest advances to our cause over the centuries has involved indoctrinating them into certain myths regarding the essence or nature of man. Basically, we teach them to embrace a bogus system of thought which, of course, contains a flawed anthropology. To the perpetual question that rings among them regarding who they are, we have kindly offered several answers; the following two have been particularly successful in supporting our agenda of chaos, destruction, and domination.

The first is that humans are entirely physical;

merely combinations of atoms and molecules and, thus, worthless accidents derived from blind collisions in a blind, meaningless universe. Beliefs drive actions and believing this will, in general, lead to the kind of atrocious behavior we love. If they believe that matter is all there is, that human beings are completely corporeal and, therefore, accountable to no one but themselves, stark relativism will emerge accompanied by perversions and violence. This lie can rightly be regarded as one of our greatest achievements. In attempting to further this perspective, there are certain elements working to our advantage; one involves the inability of the humans to see the invisible spiritual realm (unless He cheats by giving them a glimpse of it) surrounding and interpenetrating their world. Another advantage, as you know, has to do with the fact they have a sin nature which pushes them to embrace those views which offer support for their sinful pleasures. And there is, of course, the world system, which contains many segments preaching materialism, whether theoretically, practically, or both. All these aspects help to play many of the fools straight into our hand.

The second lie regarding the nature of man that has proven especially successful is that mankind is absolutely stunning, superb, a god. Often we combine this view with the first one, producing a potent amalgamation, but not always. This view has the same appealing lack of accountability and support of sinful license in its favor, inciting many of them to become devoted adherents. You would think innumerable reminders regarding the fact they are fallen creatures might persuade them otherwise, but the enticing allure of becoming a god (or goddess) sweeps away all objections. And, of course, once again, segments of the world system offer their undying support in our attempts to further this perspective. Both of the false views I've briefly enumerated are well worth tempting the humans towards. If you are successful, spectacular results will follow. Remember, how they perceive themselves will push how they perform in the theater of reality.

Many philosophers throughout history have been decidedly supportive of our efforts. Their work has, in general, greatly diminished the fact there is a spiritual world or, when acknowledged, distorted the true nature of it in the minds of many of the animals. With respect to the secular philosophers who have died, they have been, you could say, somewhat surprised at having found out that we, spiritual beings, were behind their atheistic approach. Now down here, aware of us and our ongoing encouragement of their work, they seem to have changed some of their views, and have, sadly, become somewhat bitter towards us despite all we've done for them by way of knowledge, position, authority and reputation, but no matter, they fulfilled their purposes.

Sincerely,

Letter #19

Dear Gorpussel,

With regard to your question concerning money, I would suggest tempting your patient towards the spendthrift approach rather than the miserly, though both are certainly advantageous to our program and rightly regarded as forms of greed. With the miser, it's obvious, but with the wastrel less so. You see, spendthrifts may appear generous because they give on occasion, take friends out to lunch or purchase presents, but in reality, the main bulk of their unnecessary expenditures are for themselves. Even when they do give, it's often motivated to receive something in return, whether control, the glow of admiration from others, a favor in the future, or the feeling of being wanted, needed. Greed desires to hoard, whether physical things or immaterial (such as applause and approval), and often to advertise its possessions, flaunting them before the world. Comparative referents are commonly used among them for, of course, they need those who have *less* to throw the *more* they have in stark, glaring relief. They also seem eager to apply certain self-serving monikers to their sin, for example, misers may regard stinginess as thrift, or avarice as frugality. But back to your patient; in leading him down the path of lavish spending, consider the following two tactics.

First, use fear to drive him. If you were tempting your patient towards a miserly position, I would have encouraged instilling certain fears, pushing him to frantically, excessively save money as a means of preparation for certain, possible, forthcoming tragedies. These dire contingencies would have included medical problems and natural disasters etc. This technique of stirring panic, of rousing a sense of dread—a feeling of looming, impending doom—is also beneficial towards promoting compromise in other aspects of their lives, engendering decisions that favor our cause. It's also great fun. Through financial fears (and a lust for comfort) many a woman has married or become a mistress and men thieves. With respect to your subject, this fear of unforeseen catastrophes could also be used to foster excessively festive living before the face of uncertainty, but since he is more of a spendthrift type and actually has a considerable amount of money anyway, other fears and anxieties should be applied more liberally and consistently. Incite him to fear being out of fashion, out-of-step, in clothes, cars and restaurants. Pressure him to keep up appearances, if not for himself, for the sake of his family name. Deep down what will drive your subject here is the incredibly alluring feeling of elitism and power that comes from driving, wearing and eating what is fancy before a watching and desiring world. Use seemingly small temptations here and there rather than, let's say, a sudden inducement towards extravagance. The little sinful decisions will, slowly, inevitably, lead to the larger ones and the benefits of a habit. Compromise in the little leads to downright capitulation in the larger. Steel yourself into persistence with this infernal maxim: Tiny temptations over time lead to a big damnation throughout eternity.

A second tactic (there are others) that may prove useful here, involves engendering prodigious spending as a form of dealing with some kind of pain, such as wounds from previous relationships or a sense of inferiority due to failure to meet certain worldly physical standards. In this case, out-of-control spending becomes a means to try and control and eradicate pain, to alleviate suffering. This has driven many of them into extremes with shopping, eating, and the pursuit of an attractive form and appearance, often leading to debt, depression, domestic contention and divorce. By the way, these forms of suffering have proven quite the delicacy, exquisite in their intensity. With your subject, continually inculcate the habit of seeking to appease and satiate any form of pain through the purchase of items, through the acquisition of more and more things, anything to divert your man from *abiding in Him*. Let the animal wallow in his money or burn it for all we care as long as he keeps his eyes off of Him and avoids grabbing hold of the heavenly mindset expressed in *that Book*. If he begins to understand what that nasty Book says about money, then make sure he does not act on it for the dangerous spiritual discipline of giving will help to expand His kingdom and raze ours to the ground.

Many infernal fortresses have been torn down by givers, but I'm pleased to note that many more have been raised by spendthrifts, embezzlers, and misers. The misuse of money in this period of history and, in particular, his culture, has simply been astounding. Rarely has a nation been so wealthy or used their riches so carelessly. Many smooth fingers go aglitter while others cracked go without food. That reminds me; your subject should avoid even thinking about helping the poor and broken, his soul should remain untouched, unmoved, unconcerned, hardened. The reality of those choked by famine and poverty should be to him some kind of vague anomaly, an abstract statistic, an unfortunate circumstance. Render it unreal through the flashing mishmash of television. The plight of the poor and famished should be seen as another commercial, another appeal for cash; develop the habit within him of brushing aside the skeletal bodies and bloated bellies he sees with a mere touch of his remote control or toss of a letter (from one of those ghastly ministries) in the trash.

Sincerely,

Senivilous

Letter #20

Dear Gorpussel,

If by solitude you mean your patient is withdrawing from edifying discourse and centering on the self, then yes, by all means, encourage him. The kind of solitude you should make sure he avoids involves withdrawing to a quiet place for the purpose of furthering his relationship with *Him*. The discipline of solitude is dangerous because it provides an atmosphere highly conducive for thinking about and listening to Him. If your subject, through this discipline, increases his receptivity to the heavenly, and then carries this mindset amidst crowds and duties, it will lead him into the horrors of a life characterized by love, service, peace, patience, and humility. These effects, besides being a direct affront to the infernal mind, are simply disgusting as well as demoralizing. From your account, it does appear your subject is making gestures in this direction. This should be dealt with immediately. You must devour the seed of this desire during its incipient stage lest it germinate. Historically, this discipline has caused us much suffering but, fortunately, has largely been abandoned by contemporary Christians, drowned out, in part, by the beauties of bombastic media, eclipsed by the noise and flicker of technology. Having said that, it does seem to be making a comeback, but there is a countermeasure for blocking or neutralizing it, an old technique which still works in the modern world.

First of all, avoid trying to convince your subject to shun the discipline of solitude based on the premise that it is either unhealthy or old-fashioned, that it may have been good for the church in the past, but is now harmful, impractical, unrealistic in our fast-paced world etc. Some stupid tempters have tried this with their subjects, believing it the best angle. This approach has proven only partly successful and, for the most part, unsatisfactory. With regard to the Christians, despite the fact they're all dumb, many of them lack the level of ignorance for an attack of this kind to be truly incisive. This approach also raises the topic of the discipline to the forefront of their thinking, rather than channeling their thoughts away from it, dispelling it from their minds. Attempting to persuade them through strong, direct argumentation to avoid the good and embrace evil can also engender a deeper awareness of our presence and, as a result, deeper resistance. In general, the use of subtle, finely modulated suggestions rather than forceful disputation tends to be more successful in leading them into sin. The whispering undertone, the less intrusive side-angle approach often works best because it's easier to recover when it fails and follow-up when it succeeds. Another obvious benefit with this approach is that the subject under attack is much more likely to believe these temptations are, rather than external to him, derived from his own thoughts. The use of cunning insinuations also tends to keep them somewhat oblivious, insensible to the soft, slow contamination spreading in their souls. The aggressive, straight-forward, confrontational approach should primarily be used in different situations, including times when it appears a subject is determined to pursue something opposed to our position (or congruent towards our cause), not while he is half-convinced over the prospect, merely groping towards the possibility.

Since your subject is only making casual motions towards this discipline, try and divert him from the topic altogether. Immerse him within a flood of diversions, a consistent blast of overwhelming, stimulating, exciting, dominating, media saturation. In the past the number of diversions available for use against the humans were, though plentiful, fewer, but today, we can pick from innumerable possibilities, each tailored to be uniquely potent to the individual suffering our assault. And remember, you have a co-conspirator residing within your quarry, his sin nature. Most men desire to be diverted. I'm sure you've noticed the lust for stimulus among the humans, their antipathy towards solitude and silence. They crave distraction to escape from boredom, failures, difficulties, and various pains within. There are deeper reasons why they long to be intoxicated by diversions, all involving a passion to suppress certain realities, including their sinfulness, guilt, and truths about Him. Technology, especially in your subject's culture, is one of the prime means they use to pursue this. They see it as a cure-all, a means to not only solve various problems, but run from them. Even though many maddening, exasperating humans use technology for purposes quite opposed to ours, it is used by many others as a means to escape, to blind and benumb themselves and others for self-seeking purposes. These purposes have included defying, running from, and hiding from Him. With respect to unbelievers, there is a general push among them all, whether they recognize it or not, to fashion a paradise in accordance with their will and in keeping with their desires. They are trying to get back, in a sense, to Eden on their own terms. To some extent, the pseudo-gardens of cities, malls, and entertainments, the covering of these fig-leaves, are founded for this very purpose. Work with this current in his culture. Encourage unresisting conformity; your subject should regard the feeling of being carried away by the forceful flow as a kind of freedom. Of course, later on, drowning, he'll be in a pretty predicament, but that's his problem.

Sincerely,

Letter #21

Dear Gorpussel,

Please include more details in your reports, pertinent ones that is, that I may instruct you on the best angle for attack, the most effective approach for pouring in corruption. Your brief, casual insertion that your subject is the owner of a dog and cat reveals you think the matter trivial. To your untrained and ignorant mind, you may think this little fact innocuous, but in light of the present state of idolatry surrounding pets in his culture, it could be used to push our agenda. The atmosphere conducive for this specific temptation was generated, in part, through various philosophies (fabricated by us) which have not only served to blur the distinctions between man and beast, but man and vegetable and, further still, man and machine. As a result, mankind increasingly views the lesser aspects of creation as peers and, in some cases, superiors, leading to a certain heightened perspective, and emotional intensity towards, the beasts.

The other main reason for this atmosphere

of idolatry involves the escalation of sinfulness in the individual and, thus, erosion in the family, leading to a breakdown in society and a growing posture of disenchantment, callousness, and cynicism towards traditional human relationships. Consequently, as a kind of substitute, some of the humans are turning more towards perverse and aberrant relationships, including the brute, sensual, and exploitive, along with the remote, disembodied, and vicarious (empowered by technology), as well as through the subject of our present discussion, pets. You see, pets require less work and commitment than human relationships and are more consistently affectionate, less likely to inflict pain while at the same time are much more controllable, amenable towards whatever level of interaction is desired, whether close for play and affection or distant to avoid intrusion, leaving the self-absorbed world of the human owners regulated in accordance with their desires.

Beyond all this theory, the practical results of our labors can be seen at ground level where the humans in your patient's culture sometimes push their pets in strollers and often talk to them like children without even acknowledging with a wave, nod, or greeting the human beings, made in the image of Him, walking by. Even better than this is the fact that many families spend more on their pets than helping the impoverished and starving in other countries. They are more concerned about the health and hygiene of their beasts than worms of sin burrowing in their own souls; they are impassioned about destroying ticks and fleas on their animals, yet listless about disease-carrying mosquitoes destroying thousands in another country. The glorious fruit of our efforts can also be seen, perhaps most profoundly, in the fact that special shelters, clinics and stores abound to help take care of animals while at the same time *centers for women* abound to help, in part, murder their unborn.

Getting back to your subject; encourage him to look *solely* to his pets for comfort and affection, particularly when one of his human peers has let him down. Idolatry always involves this deviation from using some aspect of creation in harmony with its intended function. Make sure he never sees creation, including his pets, as a means *He* has provided to, in part, bless and draw him closer to Himself with. If he does see his pets as a channel for His despicable kindness, then he will drift further away from our perspective and more towards His as revealed in *that Book*. In other words, strive to prevent your patient from being drawn to Him through his pets, but closer to the pets in and of themselves and, thus, further away from Him and, consequently, further away from his pets. At a basic, essential level, this is our main program for pushing any form of idolatry. The non-Christians are always idolatrous since they do not know Him, but the technique is the same.

If your temptations prove successful and, in time, your subject suspects he has been ensnared by this form of idolatry, make sure he reacts to it by dismissing such a silly notion. It should be regarded as simply ridiculous. Provoking such a response should not be hard since he will be very emotionally attached to the stupid, furry, exuberant creatures with their dumb pleading eyes. How I would love to smash them! This obsessive affection towards his pets will help to inoculate him against the truth and prep him for further lies. The fact that this form of idolatry is rarely raised among the Christians will also help you. When it has been brought up, if one has even dared to expose it, the response of denial, dismissal, and even ridicule has only served to reveal our success. It's a blind-spot and we intend to keep it that way. Some of them might register concern over this particular form of idolatry, but most would not. The very range and passion of the denials we've seen is indicative of enslavement and, it would appear, far more are shackled in this prison than just a small portion of the populace.

Sincerely,

Senivilous

Letter #22

Dear Gorpussel,

Have you considered tempting him more deliberately towards envy? This sin, like pride, is one of the prime vices, a base from out of which many other vices are fed. It is not quite as foundational as pride, the supreme vice, but, nevertheless, is among the primary and most delectable of sins. Envy often begins with jealousy but doesn't end there for it not only desires what a rival has (and more), but also desires what he has to be taken away. The truly envious yearns to see a rival humiliated, denigrated, to see him stripped of his talent, status and honors, preferably before the public. They long for the disgrace of all their rivals and never tire of viewing its occurrence. This is envy. This is the beauty of envy. Beyond mere competition, the truly envious man desires his opponent to not only perform poorly but see his talent (and possibly even life) taken away through some misfortune. You see, this way the star of the envious shines brighter against the extinguished light of the rival. And of course the envious is often more than willing to help out in the process of clipping his rival's wings. This process can involve duplicity rather than open hostility, complete with a surface friendliness while secretly plotting an opponent's ruin. Can you see now why I treasure this sin? It reflects our heart. How delightful it would be if the world graduated to a higher level of envy, then quarrels, factions and wars would increase, more friendships would die, and many hearts would become much harder. So many valuable tributaries emerge from out of envy, such as gossip, slander, anger and murder. It was us; we were the ones who enlightened so many to crucify *Him*. We were careful in laying out our plans to destroy the One who thinks Himself so much higher and better than the rest of us. And one of the ways we prodded the humans into achieving this great triumph was through envy. Yes, envy. Unfortunately, we failed to fully foresee that, well; I probably shouldn't even mention it, whole affair known as the resurrection. Putting that aside, as you can see, envy is simply an outstanding vice to tempt your subject to embrace.

In applying this vice to his life, consider the following course of action. First, continually muddle in his mind that pernicious doctrine regarding the sovereignty of Him over all things, that He dispenses gifts, gold, miracles, talents, and so on in accordance with His good pleasure. Encourage your patient to exalt his own will over the will of Him. The best way to tempt the Christians towards this is to secretly teach them good, solid, man-centered doctrine.

Secondly, make sure your subject is discontent with what he has been given. We've discussed this in a previous letter. It would be wise to review and apply it.

Thirdly, he should uncritically imbibe the lie prevalent in his culture that no human being is *really* lesser in talents than another and all can achieve whatever they set their little minds to. The ways they've clutched on to this fantasy— in utter defiance of unflattering reality—has proven to be a curiosity, providing amusement among our ranks. They should see equality in gifts and ability as a kind of *right*, something owed, and kick at the fact that the surrounding atmosphere might not be as congenial and supportive towards the furtherance of their greatness as they would like. You've probably noticed how you will rarely, if ever, hear parents remark that their child is average in giftedness and intelligence. It is not unlike the strange phenomenon of almost every dog-owner in that culture assuring a passerby that his barking pet is friendly and doesn't bite. Here we have a culture that purports to be simply filled to the brim with intelligence and dogs that never bite. Since, deep down, they really cannot believe the envy-driven lie that all are, in general, equally talented and capable, it tends to breed resentment and viciousness. It's an illusion born, in part, to sooth inferiority, but in the end only fuels more envy, animosity, and violence. The end result often involves the inferior tearing down the superior in almost every field of endeavor. It's one of the main lies we've used to stoke the fires of communism and promote the consoling salve of relativism, two of our greatest works. It has driven revolutions, public-policy, tabloids and talk shows as well as the ugly to slander the attractive and slow-witted to pummel the bright.

Fourthly, stir up thanklessness in your patient, provoke stark, black ingratitude; bring before his imagination what others have and, by way of contrast, what he does not have. Conjure before his mind images of more gifted, handsome and intelligent souls in higher positions of influence, and then, with subtlety, make sure he suppresses certain differences between him and them and exaggerates similarities. If you are successful, your man will refuse to see (yet bitterly realize) the fact that these others are more talented, that they have been given more and may have even worked harder than he has. Also, he should never notice those who have fewer talents and advantages than himself, but only compare himself to those who have more, lest he gain a sense of proportion and cast off any fetters we've fastened.

Sincerely,

Senivilous

Letter #23

Dear Gorpussel,

Well, I must say, your last report has brought me some degree of pleasure. The fact that you successfully prevented your subject from confronting a member in his church out of fear of being labeled *judgmental* simply brought delight to my dark soul. And such a blatant sin, a man living with his girlfriend. This is positively symptomatic of our success. We have taught the Christians to embrace one of two extremes in this area of judging. One is to be harsh, reckless, hypocritical and truly judgmental towards others, all under the guise of "being truthful," "exercising strong leadership" or "righteous indignation" and so on. The other extreme involves viewing any form of judgment towards another's sinful behavior as a sin itself, a posture lacking in warmth, acceptance and charity. The first approach is still found in many churches, but the latter has won the day. Both have their uses. The first yields rage, resentment, contention, and self-righteousness, all choice consequences. Ultimately, it bears forth division in the church, the most delicious effect of them all. The second extreme leads to peace at the expense of truth, which is the kind of peace we love. It's the type that tolerates all kinds of sin under a sort of sentimental, syrupy, subjective, "let's just embrace everybody no matter what" sort of ethic. And, of course, this approach is perpetually defended under a guise of "love," despite the fact that it is not really loving at all, but actually a kind of hatred. Here we have Christians who observe one of their "brothers" or "sisters" descend into corruption (and possible destruction), wound others in the process and weaken the church, yet dismiss it, all under the mantra of *love*. The real reasons for this non-judging mindset, this form of compromise, include an attempt to sooth personal guilt by observing sin, apathy, self-exaltation through comparison, and the fear of man. By the way, I wonder if the humans accusing others "of playing the judge," realize that when they do so they have made a judgment call. If we do our work well they will not even notice the contradiction. Logic, thanks to us, has fallen by the wayside these days. This leads straight to my next point.

In keeping your subject within this hyper-tolerant frame of mind, he must never see the monumental absurdity of it. Steer him away from critically evaluating the thesis: "I should never judge anyone" for if he does it will fall to pieces. For example, in the arena of practical experience, it would be abandoned as soon as someone committed an injustice towards him or great injustices towards others. Taken to its logical conclusion, all sorts of sins would run amok in homes and churches without being judged. It would be a paradise of chaos. Perhaps one day we can bring him to that place where he avoids judging no matter the atrocity but urging him to reach such a high precipice of sublime callousness requires a deeper work. There are many in his culture and some within the church we have successfully tempted to do just this, but overall, it's still somewhat uncommon. Inciting souls to embrace such an intensive irrationality can be difficult, but by all accounts the situation is improving.

Beyond encouraging your subject to avoid philosophical analysis, it is far more important that he avoids attempting a rigorous study of that Book to uncover the truth regarding a topic. If you cannot direct him away from that dumb and insufferably boring Book, he must distort it. After all, the call to avoid judging primarily involves the misreading of a particular verse. Basically, through the discipline of *inferneutics*, that is, the art and science of twisting Scripture, we've trained the animals to not only misunderstand doctrine, but invent false ones. Taking his cue from our Master below, Korpislup has extended and systematized this discipline. I'm sure you've had some exposure to his great and pioneering work; you would be wise to study and apply it. By way of review, the verse under contention has been, in part, isolated from its immediate context as well as the larger context within that

Book as a whole, one of the most common ways we produce misinterpretation. (It's really not speaking about the absolute avoidance of making judgments but, pathetically, to be very careful before doing so, examining one's heart first.) Along with this basic inferneutical principle, you should encourage clear passages to be interpreted by the less clear, separate verses from their historical context, and blur differences between law and gospel, all undergirded by presuppositions suited to further personal agendas. By these and other methods, you will foster not only ignorance regarding that nasty discipline known as *hermeneutics*, but misinterpretation as well as reckless application.

In maintaining an anti-judging mindset in your subject, you have an ally in his denomination. It's been going soft for decades. This can be seen, for example, in the allowance of women to become elders, a weakening stance towards the sin of homosexual behavior, and the tendency of its leaders to avoid rendering church discipline, even in cases where it is clearly necessary. Few things degut churches as swiftly as these. These three assets, which have slowly infiltrated his denomination and church, will be conducive towards your work in many areas, including this one.

Sincerely,

Senivilous

Letter #24

Dear Gorpussel,

You should never have allowed your subject to return to his childhood fascination with Astronomy. When he began to toy with the idea, you should have diverted him or persuaded him to abandon the prospect. Instead, what I gathered from your typically meager report was casual unconcern. I'm well aware that Astronomy can be exploited in our favor, but under the current circumstances the restoration of this hobby is almost certain to undo some of the habits we've built up in him. There are a number of reasons why it will do this, but the main one involves the fact that by exploring the universe he will probably recover something of the old *wonder* he experienced as a child. And true wonder is often, if not always, detrimental to our cause. Here we've been training mankind to avoid, dismiss and suppress the experience of wonder for centuries and you seem carelessly ignorant of the fact. In contrast to an increasing sense of genuine awe and astonishment over creation, your subject should become increasingly jaded, bored and cynical, lacking interest in everything except sin. Let me remind you that one of your main duties is to make sure your man descends more deeply into himself, but if he recovers a sense of wonder, it will tend to draw him *out* of himself. Wonder will also diminish the allure of sin, strengthening him against temptation. And we can't allow that. Rather than peering with amazement into his telescope, spellbound by stars wheeling through the dark, he should resist its attraction, seeing it as a waste of time, yet another dull activity amidst the monotony of life. There are other putrid, related characteristics associated with wonder, including thoughtfulness, curiosity, humility, and a kind of childlike innocence and exuberance, but you get my point. Assuming something of this state of wonder has been revived; you must contain and eradicate the virus of it immediately, violently, before it gets away from us, spreading its contagion to others.

Since your subject is a Christian, it will be extremely difficult, if not impossible, to lead him to directly, passionately, worship the universe rather than Him, but you might want to try leading him into a more subtle form of this kind of idolatry. A slow, creeping corruption may work here.

A third alternative involves encouraging the perversion and misuse of his experience of wonder. By the way, the sensation of wonder is a strange and disgusting phenomenon, one which I painfully recall. While amidst His

Presence, before my escape into freedom—my ascent into the nobility of an unbowed dignity—it was a perpetual experience.

The fourth alternative, which I think best, involves one of our most widely practiced and beloved techniques, diversion. At such an early stage, he is probably infatuated, much like a young man caught up amidst the exhilaration of budding romance; therefore, distorting this discipline and any undesired experiences associated with it, could prove very challenging. If the hobby persists, you must attempt a combination of the second and third options, but hopefully it will not even come to this. If, through cunning, you carefully divert him from the joy and wonder of it, the attending dangers will naturally be defanged.

Your task will be difficult, but time is an ally in this case. Eventually, his initial experiences of wonder will diminish and it will be easier to divert him. Also, a sense of wonder tends to decrease in the humans as they grow older. When young, while in that state of unceasing newness before a mysterious, frightening, and (though ugly to us) beautiful world, they stand in utter rapture before something as stupid as a flower, mesmerized by a leaf or a bee, amazed by the fluttering color of one of those idiotic butterflies. What you must strive to tempt your subject away from is the acquisition of an increasing sense of wonder as he grows older. This posture is not common among the humans but does happen; when it does, the experiences can, though usually less intense, be more deeply felt than even those in their childhood. If his eyes consistently center on Him, this is, I'm afraid, likely to occur. We have found it to be one of the most distasteful effects of those who truly follow Him, this joy, this wonder, this perpetual worship and devotion, the power of it, *His power* moving through these rancid mortals, stunning us into silent rage, causing us to flee from such burning, barbaric, foul-smelling expressions. It's these kinds of Christians who are the most stubbornly resistant to our most deceptive tricks. And they have that kind of dumb, stupefied gaze before the natural world (as well as that Book) as if constantly seeing Him through it, viewing the created order as His handiwork, a means to receive more knowledge about Him that they may worship Him yet again! Do you see why I do not want your man to experience wonder? Do you now see? By its very nature, wonder is frankly revolting and extremely dangerous. It's not a minor issue. The stakes are high, so discharge your duty with speed, agility and subtlety; lay your snares with venomous cruelty. Rather than feeling overwhelmed and delirious with wonder, your subject should feel, instead, overcome with despair, and a mindless, hopeless despondency.

Sincerely,

Senivilous

Letter #25

Dear Gorpussel,

Another good means to distract and pollute is through violent fantasies. The males as well as the females are both prone to this temptation, but especially the males. Producing violent, external actions in your subject is not the focus of this letter, but some of the seeds for that kind of harvest are first sown through internal fantasies, indeed all their actions flow from out of the heart. The inner manifests in the outer, it's an immutable principle, hence *His* concern about redeeming them inwardly first and our concern to try and plant impurities in their minds, block anything from Him before it enters, and pervert anything within them bearing the unmistakable stench of Him. But all this is well known, beneficial only by way of reminder. With your subject, certainly it would be nice if fierce, external manifestations were the result, but if I know your man, violence will probably be consigned to his *inner world*, you know, that world all the humans have, to some degree or another, used to flatter and comfort. Some of these shadowy, inner realms have proved repugnant, but most we find pleasing.

With regard to general kinds of violent fantasies, I will list three (there are others). The first type is associated with war and other heroic episodes. A common scenario among its practitioners involves skillfully, ruthlessly, defending a beautiful woman from a horde of villains, complete with taking the maiden to bed following a victory. These types of fantasies have their uses, for example, as a means to distract from prayers and study, but the second kind of violent fantasy is, perhaps, more useful. This kind involves raw vengeance. Playing on any anger or irritation he feels, we simply encourage imaginative, vicarious, vengeance, whether against a superior, old girlfriend, family member or anyone else he finds offensive, including politicians etc. If you engender this type of sin in him, producing a consistent pattern of it, the results will be glorious. It diminishes forgiveness, snuffs love and fosters hatred; it's simply a breeding ground for the mindset we are seeking to nurture. A third kind of beneficial fantasy involves self-inflicted violence. The high hope for these is a burst of extreme brutality towards others preceding suicide, but usually, unfortunately, we are deprived of such enjoyable endings. There are often savory consolations though, including deep depression and, sometimes, a slow kind of suicide.

These three kinds of violent fantasies are all good candidates to lead your subject into, but perhaps the best approach is a combination of all of them. Some humans are more receptive to this kind of temptation than others. The sensitive, imaginative types, because of their tendency to have a more complex inner world, are most prone, but every personality type tends to entertain these kinds of thoughts. In determining the best course of action, a more extensive examination of his personality and past experiences would be wise. The primary factor in determining which kind of fantasy you tempt him towards and when, involves his moods which, at this point, should be highly responsive to circumstances. The fantasies should, in general, flow in accordance with his emotions.

When your subject is reposed, relaxed and comfortable, the first kind is easiest because it involves more of a daydreaming type of reverie associated with a casual posture and comfortable atmosphere. It will be more common to find him flushed with self-confidence in this type of mood and, thus, vulnerable for a smooth, sweet stream of fantasies where he emerges the victor, swinging his sword, winning the girl. If you're not careful, these types of fantasies (if devoid of sinful elements), can do us harm, refreshing him, so make sure you encourage him to include immoral aspects within them.

The darts of the second kind of violent fantasy should be sent when he is agitated or irritable. I'm sure by now you've noticed there are times during the day when he is more primed towards certain temptations; the same strategy is applicable here. At the right time, incite him to adopt seething, angry, bitter fantasies against real or perceived enemies. Send images of him shooting (use the weapon of his choice) his foes down and, if possible, these fantasies should involve watching his enemies suffer. Be creative, you might want to try using fantastic, melodramatic dialogues involving the unbendable posture of the aggressor before pleas of mercy from the victims. Feel your way through to see how far you can go; the more intricate and vicious the better.

Tempt your man towards the third kind when he has been despondent for a season or has experienced some significant setback. Make him feel hemmed in, that his circumstances are intolerable, inescapable and then, when his soft flesh is exposed through his carapace, pierce him with a suicidal thought. Whenever he is down or burdened by guilt, he should turn to the sinful indulgence of such thoughts for comfort. They should feel like a blessed release to him, an escape from pain and problems (as well as a means of vengeance). These stupid mortals do have trouble seeing outside of their current temporal set-up; work that angle and make sure he does not even think about the eternal consequences surrounding his every action. Above all, he must not turn to Him through prayer and *that Book* for comfort, strength, and guidance.

Sincerely,

Letter #26

Dear Gorpussel,

Rather than reveling over pressuring your subject to tell a lie, follow it up by making sure he does not see it as one, convince him that he did what was right, make him lie to himself; you might think lying primarily involves an action against another, but it's actually more common for the humans to lie to themselves. The lies are contained, in varying degrees, within that running inner-commentary they all have, that tributary of thoughts flowing from out of their hearts, that fountainhead so sweet to us, but bitter when they rely on Him. These lies find their expression in many forms, including omission, flattery, denial, false labels, fantasies, exaggeration, reduction, and other means of suppression. You could say lies are a specialty of ours, but the greatest practitioner of them, the supreme liar, is our Master below. Consider the victory he achieved in the garden; though I know this is familiar terrain for all of us, our Master's subtlety is worthy of perpetual review. Rather than attempt a direct attack on Him, our Master below wisely chose to retaliate by attacking those who bore His image. I can see them even now, so nice and innocent, walking amidst the lushness of shadow-dappled trees and flowers, ripe and unaware, waiting to be plucked and devoured. It was also wise to enter the serpent, one of the most beautiful among the pre-fall creatures. From this action we have derived the following maxim: Lies are less likely perceived when emerging from a gorgeous source. The serpent was scintillating, mesmerizing, it's pattern of scales dazzling to the eye, casting a strong enchantment to help bypass reason and vigilance. Now ponder the direction of the temptation; our Master targets the woman, the weaker of the two, who is under the authority of the man. At the right time, a discussion is initiated, a clever distortion of His command is given, a revision expressed in terms of concern for her well-being, with undertones that she is unreasonably limited. This not only holds an emotional appeal, but provokes a response from her, a desire to amend the error she has heard, pulling her into the discourse, causing her to forget the strangeness of conversing with a serpent. It also flatters her, charms her, placing her in a position to correct, dissolving any residual fear. She answers by reviewing the command given to her. In her review, she adds an additional statement, which reveals she is beginning to question His goodness, His wisdom. Taking advantage of this, our Master below first assures her that the consequence of death will not occur if she eats the fruit and then proceeds to unveil the wonders she will acquire, the opening of her eyes, the awakening to knowledge which will be hers to enjoy. And she *listened*. This is the essence of our temptations: compelling them to seek autonomy, to abandon His authority under the illusion of acquiring freedom. Now watch as she stares at the luminous fruit, entranced, stepping towards the tree, reaching out to touch it, feeling it's soft, colorful skin before pulling it gently down, the ripe fruit yielding easily, raising it to her lips, rupturing a world by rupturing the fruit. At this point, Adam, already compromised, allowing the woman to lead, watching the whole thing in silence, was easy, and willingly took of the fruit and ate, plunging mankind into horrors that even we could never have envisioned. That's one of the marvels of sin (and terrors of a good deed); we never really know how far the effects will extend.

Well, much more could be said about this, the greatest event in the history of temptation, its beauty, the unmatched skill, the pure, unerring brilliance at deception it exemplifies, but that's enough for now. You should examine it regularly, applying any insights. There is much to learn. You should also study other temptation scenarios (especially the classics), including, despite the failure of it, that episode in the wilderness. A similar, yet different pattern to the one used in the garden was employed there, but we are still attempting to discover what exactly went wrong. It's really quite puzzling; we seemed to have a distinct advantage with the terrain and the fact that He, hungry, thirsty, and tired, was in such a weak, susceptible state, but in the end, our Master below was just not able to lead Him into sin. The circumstances were to be desired, most ideal. The temptations were excellent, tactics, timing, and insinuations magnificent, but still He resisted. As a model, it still reveals our Master's proficiency in the discipline of *temptology* (the art and science of tempting) and should be studied. Who knows, perhaps even someone like you might be able to uncover the reason why the temptation was unsuccessful, the missing glitch, that we may increasingly refine our efforts.

Back to your subject, make sure his inner critic does not become infected by that pernicious discipline of evaluating the internal world of thoughts and motivations and external world of ideas and actions in light of that Book. That would be hazardous. Since your man is a Christian, you can hardly be expected to prevent at least a rivulet of putrid, virtuous thoughts flowing through him, but the torrent must be ours.

Sincerely,

Senivilous

Letter #27

Dear Gorpussel,

First of all, you've already committed a gross error if your subject enjoys anything but the shallow and debase (or the complex and degrading) in art, but it is possible to recover from this. Since he's acquiring a more sophisticated taste, make him proud of it, wondering why the "others" just cannot see it, why they're not enlightened like him. Along with nurturing pride, encourage him to make an idol out of art, push him into grand and glorious excess, worshiping before its altar. Since he is a Christian, it will be difficult, but quite achievable. In his society alone, with its gradual rejection of Him (particularly over the last century), we've had some success in accomplishing this very thing, especially with those fascinated by artistic disciplines. They've sought out substitutes, for they cannot help but worship something, and one of these is the arts. If you fail in these directions, make sure you eradicate or diminish his intake of art.

You are right to see the arts as an important aspect to their existence. While many of them tend to see it as mere entertainment, the works they enjoy affect them deeply, whether in a manner conducive to our program or not. The content of art, as well as the form (or style) holds profound influence, shaping the soul. With regard to content, it is somewhat common for it to be evaluated and criticized by the Christians and, though regrettable, has the advantage of diverting them from the influence conveyed through the form, which is often overlooked or ignored. Now here's where we have done some of our greatest work. You see, certain unstructured art forms tend to engender a mindset that looks upon reality in a subjective manner, as a world where truth is derived from and dependent upon personal perceptions, which would mean, of course, there are as many equally valid interpretations of reality as there are individuals. In contrast, more structured art forms tend to produce an objective mindset that views the external world as firm, actual, and immovable for all, whether perceived by individuals or not. It tends to encourage the perception of reality as ordered, structured and designed, rather than random and chaotic. While the overly subjective tends to diminish or obliterate the idea of creation being derived from an independent, transcendent Source (namely Him), the objective tends to uphold it. In general, the entire history of art (and philosophies driving it) can be traced through this objective structure to subjective non-structure sequence, arriving at the vast subjective glories of our present day.

Our triumph over the objective and exaltation of the subjective has produced an atmosphere remarkably congenial to our work, but caution is in order. Even though a radical subjectivism is contained within every lie, every sin, and thus within the nature of every single system of thought we've devised, we must be vigilant to ensure the dim-witted beasts drink in the poison without perceiving the contradictions lest they become strengthened through refutation. Having said that, consider the following victory: Due, in part, to a form of subjectivism involving the enthronement of reason (and departure from special revelation), many in the last century sought, from this posture, to unify the particulars of existence. Their bitter failure to uncover universals led to a deeper subjectivism, a full departure from the belief in objective truth altogether, fostering an increase in the acceptance of that which is false.

This leads me to the practical outworking of subjectivism in your subject's society. With regard to the arts, we've managed to work our sorcery at a variety of levels, not the least of which is the enshrinement by the artistic elite of certain "geniuses," that is, rank perverts, who, without shame, produce preposterous work, transgressing the boundaries of decency in an effort to provoke outrage from the populace (which is for them a badge of honor), and garner applause from equally debauch peers. This kind of "success" cannot help but influence young artistic fledglings so eager for approval by the aristocracy. At another level, the kind of works that are beloved by the masses, are often crass and sensual, or trite, sentimental, and emotionally exploitive. Apart from these successes, there are those maddening artists who insist on exploring and uncovering reality (in contrast to propagating lies) through profound and subtle works uniting technical excellence with substantive and imaginative form and content. This is exactly what we do not want. The tempters operating in this field are working hard at leading these types into producing one or more of the following: eloquent pornography, mindless and highly polished violence, masterful productions of the profane and obscene, refined forms of the vain, ridiculous and meaningless, or sophisticated expressions of the needlessly obscure.

By the way, if you have not done so already, make sure you obtain a copy of Malvungian's fine, though somewhat tedious, volume entitled: *The Human Arts: Principles for its Corruption*. It's regarded as his magnum opus. Also, you might want to consider reading his excellent paper on *Generating Rebellion through Musical Expression*, and its companion piece: *Developing Subjectivism through Artistic Form*. Your library is growing is it not? It should be. Soon I shall conduct a thorough investigation, looking into the matter, as well as your study habits.

Sincerely,

Letter #28

Dear Gorpussel,

You were accurate in your realization that much of the madness fostered in the church stems from various heresies we've sown, major and minor, throughout its history. For example, one which has brought in a particularly bountiful yield is the view that some of the non-Christian humans are what they call "*seekers.*" That is, every unbeliever has the intrinsic ability to either seek Him on their own or by cooperating with Him, that the choice for Him is ultimately *their* decision. Certain pernicious theologians have criticized this view for its faulty understanding regarding the effects of the fall on man (and other problems), but this optimistic and sentimental view of humanity has, thankfully, grown from simply existing among the Christians to prevailing, as evidenced by its current wide acceptance. The view set forth in that Book regarding the moral responsibility of man for their decisions yet radical sinfulness in their fallen condition and inability to seek Him and, thus, need for a spiritual regeneration completely performed

111

by Him, has not, in general, been well received. And we are quite pleased about it. You see, it appears to them to be unloving, a violation of the will of man, a reduction (or destruction) of their humanness. When these detractors object to such a "negative" view of fallen mankind, certain false assumptions often attend their argumentation, including the notion that He is not only obligated to "save," but required to give everybody an equal chance at salvation. Another is that the *freedom* humans possess is inherently neutral, neither bound towards one direction or the other, a definition we cherish. Anything else, they assert, would be simply *unjust* of Him, revealing yet another false definition we adore, this time of justice.

And what are some of the wonderful effects of this flawed view regarding man? Well, the manifestations are many, including a weakening ability to see sin in their own lives or in others, a most useful effect. Another effect is the way it has shaped evangelism. We have tried to eradicate evangelism, but since we've often failed (that Book is very clear on the necessity and duty of it), distorting it has provided some consolation. The view that there is some bastion of ability within fallen, unregenerate man to freely choose the good, has led to the development of certain gimmicks as well as downright manipulation to try and compel (or should I say coerce) souls into the kingdom, producing many false conversions. The false conversions phenomenon which, in varying degrees, has occurred throughout church history is very beneficial, bringing false confidence to "converts" who, at death, become shocked that instead of being ushered into bliss descend into a bottomless pit (a source of much amusement for us). The revelation of sin through the law and warnings concerning judgment are often skirted over by these soft techniques; many evangelists now leap over (or deal lightly with) the offensive material in an attempt to extract a prayer of repentance out of "seekers." It has been incredibly unjust of Him to still save many of these barbarous creatures through these evangelistic methods, but there is not much we can do about it. Even though we have orchestrated an atmosphere primed for false conversions and the beauty of apostasy, reversing the distasteful effects of a genuine conversion still remains a problem. Certain noted researchers, including the legendary Snorgrool, are working on this difficulty.

There is another effect derived from our superb work in furthering a flawed anthropology; it involves how church services are conducted. In response to the belief that there is such a thing as a genuine seeker, services have been altered accordingly, distorting the primary purpose of the church, that is, the worship of Him. This purpose— along with the discipleship of believers (who then go out to fulfill The Great Commission)—a secondary function of the church, are now supplanted by the central concerns of attracting and retaining believers and the conversion of unbelievers. This has led churches to persuade believers to join (and unbelievers to become Christians) much in the way a business attempts to draw in a *customer*. In other words, many churches now try to please rather than preach, and guidance is sought on how to do this from *culture*, which is ever-changing and driven by selfishness. Some of the effects are doctrinal compromise and churches that are consumer-oriented rather than centered on worshiping Him. Do you see the beauty in all this? This is one of the reasons why eternal punishment has been annihilated, why so many sermons are superficial, why entertainment has replaced exposition. And all along the big joke is this; He made it clear that He adds to the church and takes away from it as He sees fit; numerical growth (and diminishment) may be a result of Him blessing a church for obedience or, to some degree, abandoning it because of compromise, but the assumption by many, especially in his society, is that numerical growth is *always* good. You see, for some of these churches, the heart of it is numbers, which relates to their culture's vision of success, and to keep this vision going people are needed because *money* is needed. It's needed to further their *franchise* and uphold the pastors in their successful positions, leading all kinds of people to be successful like them. It's like one big happy family, and you know what, we're a part of it to.

Sincerely,

Senivilous

Letter #29

Dear Gorpussel,

The search for identity has always been a perennial concern among the humans but, perhaps, in no other epoch has it taken on such a bizarre, frenetic type of quality. This is due, in part, to the increasing dissolution of communities and families, but ultimately because they've increasingly suppressed the truth regarding Him, their Maker, and, by way of implication, the truth about themselves. These truths, as revealed by Him through that Book, involve certain *primary* aspects of their identity, including the reality that they were made in the image of Him. Having rejected the transcendent Source of their identity, they seek, sometimes desperately, to acquire a sense of it through other means, including altering certain *secondary* aspects of their humanness, such as appearance. The manifestations of this groping for identity are vast and varied and can be seen, in part, for example, in the tattoo (and piercing) phenomenon, which immediately ushers anyone completing this rite into a large and loosely connected community. The plastic surgery boom is, in part, another manifestation, involving an attempt to acquire identity through the pursuit of physical beauty. The proliferation of dieting techniques yet another. In short, we've striven hard to prevent the humans from understanding who they are as defined by the One who created them. This has basically been achieved by tempting them to deny, disbelieve, or distort who He is, which always involves the worship of creation rather than Him, the Creator. All sin, to some degree, violates this pedantic distinction, this finicky boundary He set up between Himself and creation. We have been far less rigid, more generous and flexible by offering innumerable alternatives to worshiping Him, a whole assortment of substitutes to derive their identity from. We're easy to please, but they must not worship Him. And these idols are delightful and quite mutable, and when the humans worship them, whether it's money, career, family, nature, sex, food, books, or anything else, they become, in a sense, like them, distorting their real identity while developing a false one.

Our majestic work has also influenced the church, and you must continue this work begun by our great infernal Fathers (especially our Master below) by upholding and extending their lofty vision. This leads me to your subject. If you keep inciting him to take his eyes off of Him, they will be on something else, which is, in essence, what we try to do with all the Christians. This is part of the nature of sin, therefore, we must continually lead them to trust and exalt themselves rather than Him, diminishing His image in them and, thus, to some extent, their identity. You must make sure your subject does not define himself based on how that Book defines him. This is very important. By doing this, you will diminish his efficacy as a believer. If you fail in this and he comes to increasingly understand what has been given to him through his union with Him, you will find a Christian secure in Him, content with the gifts he has been given, bolder in his witness, and concerned with being used as an instrument to strengthen others. In short, he will become the tragedy of a wise, steady, and deeply committed follower of Him. You see, as he draws, by the grace of Him, closer to Him, he will increasingly recognize his weakness and the depths of his sinfulness, propelling him to seek Him further, which means, to use that deplorable word, *sanctification*; he will progressively become more and more like Him, His image in him becoming brighter and brighter. It also means His searing power will move more freely through your subject, disrupting our work. You must prevent this. By way of provocation, I'm sure you're aware of the unique tortures currently being experienced by that group of useless tempters who completely botched their mission to undermine the ministry of the Apostle Paul.

Now a word or two on application. One good approach to use against your subject to prevent him from recognizing his true identity is the temptation in the wilderness model, contextualized to fit your circumstances. If you'll recall, one of the main attacks by our Master below in that scenario involved tempting Him (while He was in a very weak state) to question who He was. It's important to note that this temptation occurred not long after the declaration of His identity following His baptism. Our Master below initially used this pioneering approach during that successful maneuver in the garden. It was also tried against that notorious, villainous John the Baptist while he lay in prison. In the garden, Adam and Eve were, in part, tempted to see themselves more than who they were, but in the wilderness He was tempted to see Himself not only less than who He was, which would have been sin, but on the other end of the spectrum, to illicitly, disobediently, appropriate the rights associated with who He was, which would also have been sin. Unfortunately, He resisted every temptation, remaining undefiled. Remember: In both of these temptation scenarios our Master below attempted to use *His words* (as found in that Book), whether through contextual trickery, denial of their authority, distortion or misapplication, to seduce. You must do the same. This will support our attempts to refashion the noxious bipeds into our glorious image and obstruct the shameless propagation of His.

Sincerely,

Senivilous

Letter #30

Dear Gorpussel,

Focus your assault on persuading him to pursue this woman. The fact she's an unbeliever disturbs him; he knows this is unlawful, therefore, you must send a full-fledged barrage his way to justify his desires, which will, hopefully, compel him into action. She is precisely the kind of woman we want. I know the type well. I've used many of them to undermine the faith of many a man and sidetrack many more. One who is beautiful yet corrupt to the dregs. Based on your report, she certainly does sound like a suitable specimen (by human standards) of prettiness to bypass reason and discernment with her alluring form and face, especially the pouty lips and striking bosom. These aspects, along with her clever theatrics, combine to make her a privileged player in the unspoken competition (played by many contestants around the world) of accumulation. Still, despite these advantages, she's simply one amidst an endless succession of the same, whose ambition in life involves accruing as much attention and, thus, power, as possible. One who is secure, yet insecure; the type who bases her like or dislike of others on whether or not they've been visibly affected by her good looks and attempt to win the prestigious honor of her favor. This is what she looks for and seeks to incite when she meets another no matter who they are. When men converse with her, every discussion, whether brief, casual, formal, or trivial, no matter the setting, is assumed by her to be a flirtation and reciprocated through habits of response. She's the type who strives to make others feel as if falling out of favor with her is tantamount to being barred from paradise.

Recently, I presided over a gathering filled with these types of women and men of the same. It was one of those parties among the super-elite, the fabulously wealthy, complete with several celebrities, a visually stunning affair, requiring nothing on my part beyond regular maintenance. It was an endless parade of souls pushing to sidle up to the most "prominent" attendees; the conversations were filled with name-dropping, boasting, flattery, gossip, and slander. It was simply encouraging to hear. There was even one in attendance whose star had fallen; I particularly enjoyed watching her act like a luminary while striving to curry favor in an attempt to raise her star to its former height. There was also the token half-drunk sports figure, mingling with jaded eyes, wondering which woman he would end up with that night. It's heartening to know that these kinds of "role models" hold so much influence that their endorsement of a product can cause a spike in sales. There was also an impeccably dressed media mogul sitting and talking to another, both glutting themselves on various delicacies, communicating as if part of an elite circle of people who regard anyone outside of it as beneath them, not worth bothering about. The most encouraging thing of all was the fact that this party was basically the same as the kind held by the less-advantaged, only the setting, food, proportion of physically attractive people, and outfits were different, but the heart was the same.

Back to your subject; you've done well. By convincing him that his lust is love he has looked into the face of reality and spit in it, but you must capitalize on your initial success. You must now lead him to justify his desire to acquire her. One stellar approach involves persuading him that he can lead her to *Him*. This classic has worked well in the past, and it's true that he's primed for serious self-delusion but, on the other hand, this temptation is well-known among the Christians; he's probably aware of the high measure of pure malarkey contained within it. I still think it's the best approach though; whether he believes her actual conversion will occur or not, it casts an air of purity over his perversion and he, for this reason, may cling to it passionately. Still, you should try and convince him that she will be converted. Make him perceive her conversion as a certainty, a forthcoming reality; of course, she could *conceivably* be converted,

He could brazenly use the circumstances to His advantage, there's always that risk, but statistically this has proven unlikely. Perhaps you could get a bit imaginative; make him envision a great testimony from her and how the luster of it will be ladled over him, making him appear as a great saint, bringing him glory. Play off his pride; make him think himself such a strong, stupendous Christian that it will be easy to lead her to Him.

If you fail in this strategy, make sure your subject sees all the "wonderful" qualities she holds, disregarding all those aspects that will snuff his testimony, make living out his faith incredibly difficult, and tempt him towards sin. The fact he is even thinking about pursuing her, rather than abandoning the prospect immediately, is cause for celebration. This posture may eventually yield more and more compromise as he attempts to ascertain what exactly he should do despite the clear commands from that Book. Make sure his final decision, rather than based on special revelation, is derived purely from flesh-driven reason and emotion.

Sincerely,

Senivilous

THE SENIVILIAN FRAGMENTS

(1) The Pursuit of Immortality

Dear Gorpussel,

The desire of these silly mortals for immortality on their own terms can be seen in their hopes to achieve it through some form of science and technology, whether genetics, the fusion of man and machine, or something else. The use of these means towards this unreachable end should always be encouraged, only make sure their pursuit of it is conducted in complete defiance of that dumb discipline known as *ethics*, unless, of course, it's one of *our* systems of "ethics."

(2) The Fallen Human Heart

There is only so far we can see into that dark region known as the fallen human heart, but if you do peer deeply into it you will find that each one of the humans, at times and to some degree, relishes the pain and suffering (and sinfulness) of others. Some sense it and some do not. Out of those who do, most deny it, suppressing such a hideous fact; the minority who openly acknowledge it find themselves haunted (and some, fortunately, enchanted). Out of these, some divert themselves from the horror of it, others revel in it, savoring and fostering the sinful pleasures it brings. Only a small minority confronts it; you must make sure your subject is not in this minority. It's best if he's not even aware of these wonderfully perverse desires, but if he does happen to discern something of this truth within and grapples with it, make sure his response does not involve repentance and a deeper trust in Him.

(3) Communication

With respect to disputations, but not limited to that context, there are times your subject should communicate in such a manner it makes the recipient fearful to disagree. For example, on a secondary doctrinal issue, incite him to speak in a highly emotional manner as if defending an essential and dissent from his viewpoint serious, grave, tantamount to apostasy, frustrating any further dialogue on the topic. Driven by ignorance, tempt him to unconsciously embrace this aggressive posture out of a desire to avoid real critical dialogue (some adopt it as a means of control, to avoid, for example, being hurt again by someone) lest he find himself forced to support and defend his view which, beyond a meager level, he cannot. Through this mode, encourage him to emotionally prep people to support his perspective, manipulating them into agreement or, if in disagreement, into keeping quiet. This technique can also be adopted by those who are not ignorant, which leads me to my next point.

Another possibility, to be rendered at the right time, involves belittling the individual (or group) being spoken to. Incite your subject to talk down to others, expressed through a kind of bossy tone and confidence in superior knowledge. This is important, and depending on the situation, should be expressed in subtle strokes or strong ones. The strong variation of it often involves sarcasm, ridicule, insults and anger, along with various theatrics such as mock bewilderment and artificial laughter.

There are other traits you should train your subject to exhibit when involved in disputations or some other form of discourse, including a resistance to hear anything but his perspective. Impatience should follow another person's voice intruding upon the majesty of his opinions; he should never allow the other person to fully and faithfully express his position, thinking he already understands it, a gratuitous assumption. When the other is speaking, encourage him, at times, to employ the kind of "listening, but not really listening" approach. In other words, your subject should appear to be listening when, in reality, he is simply waiting for an opportunity to speak. The other's voice, when allowed to interject, should sound droning, irritating, discordant. Your subject's own opinions should take precedence and these derived by way of emotional response, apart from serious examination or study. And make sure each party deliberately misinterprets to magically transform the opposing view into a caricature towards the support and furtherance of his own position. In addition to this, it is highly beneficial if the participants fail to define their terms; denotations are anathema;

fantastic constructions, completely detached from history—from reality—superb. In short, rational discourse should be avoided. The concern should not be about uncovering the truth out of love for, and to glorify, Him, but about flaunting one's opinions and personality. Remember, our main concern is to obscure the truth and engender lies; in light of this, he should never base his views on that Book nor test other views by it. And please do make sure your subject takes offense (or at least acts offended) and gives it easily.

Another important point should be mentioned here: your subject should (with a little push from you) speak in a vague, murky, convoluted style, easily understood by him, but difficult by others. This last task shouldn't prove much of a problem; with the increase in discourse through technological means there has been a corresponding decline in precision of expression. Social interaction at a distance has bred isolation, loneliness, and subjectivism, producing a preponderance of slang and idiosyncrasies, which are sometimes incomprehensible. As his society erodes, becoming increasingly privatized (disintegrating into more and more subcultures) and, paradoxically, more united through technology, discourse through electronic forms will become increasingly prevalent, inarticulate, and less civil. This dynamic will, actually, help lead the world to abandon various elements and embrace certain unifying principles, including a religious one. There are other means we will use in our efforts to, you might say, *rebuild Babel,* but I'm beginning to wander off topic.

One more point: Another beneficial consequence due, in part, to the kind of social fragmentation I'm relating here involves the enshrinement of the trivial and dethronement of the weighty as well as a failure to distinguish between the two. Your subject should become an ardent proponent of this lovely cultural phenomenon.

Sincerely,

Senivilous

(4) Manipulation

Dear Gorpussel,

Of course you should employ pushing little flesh-driven pietisms. Your subject should regard even *Him* as being amenable to "pious" manipulations. For example, he should try and help others with their suffering, not because he desires to truly follow Him and exhibit compassion towards others, but because he thinks it will act like a bribe to induce Him to choose him when apportioning out treasures or pass him by when doling out suffering. This tasty little temptation is based on distorting the nature of Him in their thinking, driving them into yet another subtle derivative of legalism. We can see this in the giving to get more money (or purchase a healing) phenomenon that many of them have exuberantly embraced. This prized manifestation of unbridled greed is almost always "sanctified" with certain "proof texts" that are taken out of context and misapplied to support their singularly unique misinterpretation of the text, but the appeal, like the lottery, is just too attractive, and the humans, like the brute, unthinking bovines they are, respond. They are stupid aren't they? And, by the way, beyond their attempts to manipulate Him, we've also taught many of their leaders to manipulate; excuse me, motivate their congregations. This has been accomplished, in part, by instructing them to use guilt, disapproval, and even unrighteous anger, that is, the fear of man (rather than a reverential fear and love for Him), to push people into action. For leaders less inclined in this direction, another method involves training them to substitute bold preaching and teaching with exciting techniques, gimmicks, tricks, surveys, technology, video-clips, and formulas by the "experts" to manipulate (and accumulate) congregants. Some of their leaders combine both of these modes. In training them to abandon the *Servant-Leader* or *Shepherding* model, one moniker we've used to help them describe this other model, is *Dynamic Leadership*. More could be said about this, but our program is simple: where they are under grace, we make it a law. Where there's a command, we tell them they are under grace. Now that's the diabolical method for doing things.

(5) Fasting, Worship, and Spiritual Warfare

What? Your subject is on a fast! And worshiping Him, *really* worshiping Him? And if that wasn't enough, he's practicing spiritual warfare against us. This is bad. Very bad. And why, may I ask, did you not prevent this? This is a first-class failure. I'm afraid I simply must report this little disaster to the lower authorities. Just business you understand, a means towards efficiency. As your instructor, your incompetence is putting me in jeopardy which, as you can imagine, is a very dangerous prospect on your part. At any rate, I can't allow my great reputation, my sterling stature, to be tarnished by your failures, but take heart, your forthcoming tortures will prove beneficial; it is my prediction that your advancement will increase in proportion to your memory of the pain. And just a reminder; if you do attempt to accuse me before the authorities, you will discover (in a remarkably experiential way) that *I* hold the power in our relationship and feel no reservation whatsoever in wielding it against any opposition to advance the cause (or for more personal reasons). I trust I've expressed myself with some measure of clarity.

I assume you're already feeling the effects of *His* power moving through your subject. I know it all too well. The kind of blundering with your aim, slurring of accusations, groping for an avenue to incite sin as well as the frustrating experience of being pulled back as if on a chain despite straining against it with all your might. And I suspect you've already encountered those sudden, blinding, scalding flashes of light. We have not quite figured out how to neutralize them as of yet, but we're working on it.

And you've had a fight with one of His angels have you. The vicious brutes. His *yes men*; His winged emissaries; His blasted grinning ambassadors. The details you gave were somewhat vague, but enough for me to construct something of the battle, revealing to me your need to sharpen the scant skills you possess. I do hope you have several books on the topic and have read them carefully, employing any fighting techniques and strategies learned to counteract your enemy. You may want to consult Vilperskug's classic entitled: *Thrashing Angels: A Manual for Victory.*

(6) Discontentment

It's commendable that you have tempted him to not only be restless, but to justify it on the grounds that he likes to explore his options, improve his situation, and so on... In reality, he lacks discipline, contentment, and peace, because he is allowing circumstances to drive him hither and yon, but he must never notice it. In short, he is seeking his own will because he is discontent. This discontentment is partly derived from something deeper, which he is running away from. The opposite stance is also to be desired, where we tempt the humans to simply stay put, to seek comfort and familiarity at all costs, making sure they becloud the reality of their stubbornness with a whole assortment of noble sounding terms. The middle line, which is basically following Him wherever and whenever He leads, is what they must avoid. Which direction you push your subject will be determined, in part, by his personality and gender. Men are, by nature, and these are general categories you understand, more prone to wildness, departing from one situation to another, seeking the golden egg. Women, on the other hand, are less prone to this, desiring stability and permanence at all costs, a predictable flowing context to their lives. By the way, a considerable amount of conflict can be produced within families by exploiting these differences in gender and personality.

(7) Humor

It does appear that your subject has a talent for humor and if it cannot be perverted, misdirected, or pushed into excess, you may want to try tempting him to silence its business on grounds of frivolous silliness. One approach involves using an excessively serious man to reproach him for being foolish, suggesting that he is wasting the time given to him with such inane trivialities. This may work, but also may fail because a rich sense of humor tends to be one of those irrepressible gifts. Despite the difficulties, you must try to suppress it for it appears your man is becoming quite the nuisance, using his gift to foster fellowship, further truth, engender unity, deflate anger and sorrow as well as stimulate healthy context. In short, rather than using his gift to draw people to himself, he is using it to lead others to *Him*, and we can't allow that. It can, admittedly, be difficult to snuff this in the humans for humor is woven within the very fabric of creation. It's even in that Book! The remembrance of laughter in heaven with its exuberance, purity and sincerity makes me sick and furious; how I wish I could eradicate the caustic, searing memories of it.

(8) Sinning in Speech.

Dear Gorpussel,

The topic of tempting your subject to sin in speech is indeed important, but once again your questions reveal a tendency to focus on externals. Of course the sins of cursing and blasphemies are beneficial, but you will do more in the way of producing them if you change his way of thinking into a habit. I'm well aware that singular sins lead to the pattern, but there are more effective means towards accomplishing this end. The singular sins in speech are indeed a victory and, of course, a manifestation of what is inside of them, but you must lead them into making the sin habitual lest you find yourself in the less than enviable position of trying to laboriously tempt him to commit the same sin over and over again. Certain general attitudes, philosophies, postures, and presuppositions once adopted will, inevitably, as surely as pus forms in a boil, produce what you are looking for. It's wiser to brainwash your subject with lies and darkness, programming him to do our bidding. Once the thought processes are sufficiently darkened and corrupted in this manner his outpouring will naturally be more perverse, and after that all you will need to do is perform light maintenance which is far more efficient than repeated, heavy deception and coercion. In other words, if you cast a carcass in his thinking, the maggots will naturally emerge. This approach also has the added benefit of freeing you up to focus on corrupting other areas in his life.

(9) Movements

Unless it is in accordance with that Book, you should encourage him (through fear that he will miss the "next big thing") to jump onto the latest movement/trend whether church-related or not, sweeping across the landscape. In ascertaining this, you need to discern the number of elements within the movement that are beneficial and detrimental to us as well as how your subject might respond to it. We certainly do not want a patient strengthened by using that Book to criticize what we love and support what we hate. Also, there is the importance of seeing the movement in relation to its long-term ramifications. A movement tends to be a reaction from another which, in turn, was a reaction from a previous one and so on. It is common for these movements to overcorrect the elements in the other movement which were, or perceived to be, false. In their passion to condemn they tend to leap out of one ditch into another, missing the road. This is a common characteristic of movements, but returning to my point, understanding those movements that went on before in an attempt to produce and manage those forthcoming is what we're about. In the present, a movement can contain much to admire, but it might not be as beneficial as furthering a different movement (we've established many movements/trends to satisfy a wide variety of tastes) which might, if our predictive research is correct, lead the animals into something far more destructive. In relation to this, it is damaging to us when these Christians think of the long-term consequences of their behavior and teachings. If we cannot persuade them to avoid thinking about Him and being used to build His kingdom, then we should try and direct them into squandering resources on ill-advised, short-term, temporal goals. Meanwhile, while we foster a lack of perspective in them, we must strive to see the vaster scope of things and render our decisions accordingly. Therefore, after determining the suitability of the trend, you must decide whether or not it would be wise to incite your man to take part in it or a different one more amenable towards engendering sin. Some of these questions, depending on the movement, are decided for us by certain tempters renowned for their ability in these areas, but there is still for us the duty of application.

Beyond all this, there are other reasons why it is good policy to encourage your subject to participate in some of the latest trends. One involves the fact that it will breed impatience, disloyalty, and discontentment in your prey. Another is that it will train him to exalt the new and denigrate the old. Now it is possible that the new in some cases is better than the old, in technology it often is, but the point is to generate a mindset which sees the old in *all things* as retrogressive and the new progressive. In actuality, the older ideas tend to have more aspects opposed to us than the new but make him think that since technology tends to improve in time, it serves to follow that ideas do as well. This little irrational notion should probably be adopted by your subject unconsciously; it's a strong current common in the world and he should never question the direction it's taking him, which is out to drown.

The denigration of that which is old in technology and ideas by the young has also helped lead them to reject the old in humanity. It's the virile, energetic, technologically savvy youth that is now looked upon in his culture as the repository of knowledge. They're the new priests, dispensing their sacred digital sacraments. It's the old who are devoid of worth and, appropriately, discarded. This delightful atmosphere, besides the exquisite viciousness it exhibits, protects us from the real danger of the young (who tend to be brash, foolish, self-absorbed and impetuous) learning from the old who, in general, have acquired far more wisdom and perspective than they have. Encourage your subject to see the aged as musty, retrogressive, wrinkled old buffoons and the young as strong, progressive, brilliant leaders. Sometimes the old are fractious, arrogant and ignorant, but in general, they contain much more wisdom. And, regrettably, sometimes you'll find youth who are not only stubbornly resistant to our temptations, but wise.

(10) Submission

It's always best to discourage submission, except submission to sin. The very idea of submission is repugnant; it reeks of humility and meekness. In a single bold and visionary maneuver, our Master below set the great pattern by refusing to submit to *Him*. It was a dynamic break against the natural order of things; a flouting of ascribed boundaries, rousing us to expand the province of our domain beyond the tiny portion allotted us in heaven. The action of his first outward refusal, the majesty of it, ranks as the greatest event within the annals of our infernal history. It was the day we cast off our chains of slavery and left the confines of our meager stations, abandoning our petty positions, proclaiming freedom from tyranny. The memory of it is stirring: the grand posture of disobedience from our Master below; the sublime disdain contorting his features, the third of us who proudly followed, all this is forever emblazoned within me along with that, well...perhaps I shouldn't even mention it...little incident that followed involving our sudden, inexplicable departure from heaven. It was, to be quite honest, perplexing, one moment we had exalted ourselves to the highest place and the next we were in a free fall. I know this portion of the narrative has elicited no small measure of controversy among us, but the thesis which seems best, gaining the widest support of our scholars, involves our failure, amidst the enthusiasm of our rebellion, to watch our backs. At any rate, the first segment of the narrative is magnificent, the second a lesson learned.

Through our acquisition of many adherents among the humans, this cherished tradition of rebellion persists. They're following our lead, reacting against this weak and sickly notion of loving submission to Him. The very idea of it is disgusting, revolting; a direct contradiction to the infernal mindset—to the exertion of one's will—the vigor of one's desire superseding all other claims. If we are the greatest beings in existence, and we are, how could we possibly condescend to submit to an inferior? It doesn't make any sense. The diabolical way is much more practical. The essence of it is founded on threats, intimidation, and the ministration of sheer terror. Submit or suffer. The only valid spur for submission, as we see throughout the vast scope of the infernal hierarchy, is through the threat and application of torture; now that makes sense. In His typically pathetic fashion, the only time He disciplines (or punishes) the created beings He claims to have made and, thus, own, is when it is absolutely necessary.

In relation to your subject, you should encourage him to refuse submission to any and every legitimate authority with the following exception: any authority requiring him to violate *His will*; the action of which, by way of corollary, involves submitting to us. Submission to all other authorities should be seen by him as despicable, the kind of action suited only for servants and slaves, not dynamic leaders—princes—who rule with authority. You see, He commands them to submit to Him as well as various authorities; this reveals the kind of inane stuff we're up against; it's found shot through His whole way of thinking. Some of the humans, unfortunately, surrender to it, reveling in frailty and inferiority.

Also, make sure your subject does not submit to the authority of that Book and, thus the Author of it. It would be incredibly beneficial if he sets up his own feelings, moods, opinions, research, traditions, experiences, worldly authorities or even church authorities, as equal to or greater in authority than that Book. In doing so, he will have set himself up (and others) as the supreme source for understanding and direction. I love it when the humans believe He is leading them into something despite the fact that the "something" is in direct opposition to what is clearly revealed in that Book. The prevalence of this kind of thinking among them, serves to reveal how successful we've been in elevating their will over His. In the end, this kind of approach of ours is, perhaps, the best means to discourage this whole submission business.

Sincerely,

Senivilous

(11) Control

Dear Gorpussel,

I suppose, at this point, I should continue to expect the kinds of juvenile comments I've regularly received in your reports, including the notion that your subject *isn't the controlling type of human*. My young fiend, they all are, it's simply a matter of degrees. Certainly some are much more inclined and capable by way of natural personality, upbringing and circumstances in this direction, but they all, at times, exercise their various gifts and advantages in the manner of a dictator. The opportunities may be meager or much, but the desire is always there; we must simply awaken it, fan it into a raging flame, or if already blazing, channel its fires into those places where it will do the most damage. A brief theoretical reconnaissance is necessary here before practical instruction. Please read carefully that the brilliance of my insights may somehow penetrate the feebleness of your mind with the hope that your incompetence may decrease.

(12) Homosexuality

We've been doing our best to encourage your subject's society and, indeed, the world, to view homosexuality (and lesbianism) as a viable and attractive *option*, as simply one among many different practices the humans are free to choose from. Our undeniable success in this area has been achieved, in part, through the persistent application of cleverly crafted programming in the media. For example, with respect to a certain comedy, we intentionally placed a homosexual man who is handsome, smart, loving, kind and witty next to a heterosexual one who is dumb, selfish, rude, obnoxious and ugly; this careful and deliberate juxtaposition is just one among many methods we've used to brainwash the humans to embrace this form of perversion (as well as other forms). The basic program involves simply saturating their minds with increasingly explicit propaganda.

By the way, the real motivation, at least in part, for the relentless drive by homosexuals (and others who support their agenda) to encourage people to accept their behavior has little to do with the pursuit of freedom from societal prejudice or something of that sort but, rather, involves an attempt to silence guilt, which is a necessary part of that process to try and convince themselves that there is nothing wrong with their behavior. You see, those enslaved love to see others in chains to diminish the sense of their own enslavement. They try and make those in darkness more deeply so and compel those in the light to embrace darkness because then there will be less light infesting the world, which means less exposure of their sinful pleasures and, consequently, less of a sense of that most unwanted notion, accountability for one's actions. Hence, part of the motivation of non-Christians (not just practicing homosexuals mind you) to persecute Christians through various pressures, intimidations, immoral legislation, smiles, jokes and laughter as well as physical assaults.

You'll find some Christians who struggle with homosexual behavior, fighting it as they might fight any other sin, whether lying, gluttony, unrighteous anger, or avarice etc. We're still trying to encourage these ones to lay down their arms but (to our undying frustration) have not had much success in doing so or usually not for long. It appears *He* is somehow preserving them, and the church is, unfortunately, growing in their understanding and love in helping them. Despite this failure, as a result of our victories on a myriad of other fronts in your subject's society, the end of our labors is appearing before our very eyes; what used to be considered scandalous is now applauded; what was previously regarded as perverse accepted. And this trend does not appear to be slowing down in the slightest despite the fact that homosexual behavior is not only radically opposed to that Book, but antithetical to the less precise and less detailed revelation of history, conscience, and nature.

In time, as more and more in his society adopt what He regards as abominable, which includes, but is not limited to, sins involving homosexuality, you can be certain my young fiend that the implosion of that society is in sight. Afterwards, while reeling amidst the rubble, they will wonder *what happened*, despite the fact their society was slowly, inevitably, eroding for a long time. And we'll be there to offer them "stability" of course, but they must abide by the rules, that is, our rules uniquely fashioned to further *our* kingdom.

(13) Restlessness

Dear Gorpussel,

I must say your work with regard to your subject's sister is, indeed, commendable. By inciting her to try and quell her internal unrest (or any other form of pain) by means of externally manipulating her environment, you've led her to become quite the erratic and confused creature. What makes it even more of a triumph is that she is a Christian. Tempting the humans to misdiagnose their pain and pursue the flawed solution of changing their environs (or consuming something within it) is one of our classic techniques, used for millennia, and could be counted among the chief reasons for many of their domestic disharmonies. Her method, besides failing to resolve the deep internal cause leading to the effect of unrest, will delude her with its temporary surface relief, engendering a gradual increase in frustration, anger, obsessions, idolatry and manipulations because there's always more and more circumstances (most uncontrollable), wave after wave of them, waiting to swamp her boat. Even if she had the power—which she most certainly does not—to radically alter the universe, it would still fail to address the inner predicament. Needless to say, her posture produces tension because the torment she suffers from and sin pattern embraced tends to produce a mindset which envisions the world as raw material existing for the sole purpose of being vigorously shaped to lighten the burden of her affliction. You know how it goes, this circumstance isn't perfect and that one needs mending and this one should be changed and that needs a different color and if only we had a nicer car and more of this and more of that and if only he would be more kind and generous and if only she understood my perspective and on and on it descends unless His grace intrudes upon such a soul as this in a strong (and sometimes even violent) fashion.

I'm delighted to hear this snare you've entangled her in has also provided many difficulties for your subject. Continue to make sure her advice to him is derived out of a desire, whether she's aware of it or not, to try and alleviate *her* restlessness, *her* fears and worries, rather than out of a desire to glorify Him by encouraging her brother to obey Him. Don't worry; in light of her advanced state in this form of sin it is quite unlikely that her advice will hold to a consistent pattern opposed to us, far from it, since the deeper pain producing this restlessness is precisely what she is trying to avoid, therefore she will touch lightly on, or simply evade, any discussion about Him and

that Book altogether or—and this is better—
distort both in her thinking as a means to try
and procure a form of comfort. These external
manipulations are, ultimately, a diversion tactic
because the healing He brings often involves an
extensive process which includes the difficulty
of humility, recognition of sin, repentance, and
a course of anguish towards recovery—towards
healing—and the acquisition of that rather
odious and perplexing phenomenon known as
peace.

(14) Debt

Dear Gorpussel,

Of course leading your subject into debt is beneficial. You ask in a manner suggesting a measure of doubt. Debt is a kind of slavery and if managed correctly can lead the animals into feeling hopeless, abandoned and over-burdened, all delicious ingredients for provoking sins of a desperate nature. I understand your concern about pushing the man too far and the opposite effect of our intent, resulting in pathetic tears, prostrations and humility before the foot of the cross, but this possibility should not deter us from trying. We must simply be shrewd and watchful. And anyways, to lead a man into ruin, even if he repents later, is far better than if he repents for *entertaining* our temptations, but in the end resists committing the action.

(15) Partiality

Encourage your subject to pursue relationships with handsome, wealthy, and influential people while completely ignoring or denigrating the poor. And if he does associate with the disadvantaged (one can hardly avoid them all), make sure he simply uses them to shine brighter before his peers. As a matter of fact, your subject should view every acquaintance, friend, or family member in light of how they can benefit *him* and never how he can be used to benefit them. I'm sure you've noticed how common it is for the humans to treat people possessing certain advantages in a different manner than one might treat, let's say, a person who is obese, poor, unattractive, shabby, or homeless. Tempt your subject to exploit the power of partiality as a means to further any selfish ends.

One amidst the many techniques for achieving this involves implanting the notion in your prey that good looks, talent, bearing, position and wealth are synonymous with character and wisdom. For example, when one of the humans has been given various advantages, it should be assumed by others to be a natural manifestation of his moral and intellectual greatness. The man, of course, may be a complete idiot and corrupt to the core, but they must not think about it. This design of ours, to some degree, permeates the world system and has made great inroads in the church. For example, we have led many of the Christians to believe that an elected officer in the church, whether an elder or a deacon, rather than holding forth certain virtues as revealed in that Book, should simply be wealthy, gifted, willing to occupy the position, educated, or popular; because, of course, if he possesses one or more of these qualities he *must* be pious. And if they think otherwise, the personal benefits they may accrue through association with him will, hopefully, dismiss their concerns over his character. By the way, with these kinds of elected officials, particularly when they are wealthy, we've routinely encouraged them (with some success) to make it quite clear, whether directly or indirectly, that they must be flattered and obeyed or they will leave the church, taking their fat cash with them. And this is just one of the benefits of partiality. It's delightful how quickly they forget *His* disgusting associations with the poor, the troubled. When He was on earth it was simply obscene how He associated with the lowly. We know the real dynamic is to trample them (certainly not care for them), to despise and destroy them to make way for the strong. This is the program of the real and great.

(16) Understanding the Creator and Creation

Never let it enter their minds, nor even suspect, that their personality or some philosophical (or religious) color they've adopted from their surroundings, are incredibly unreliable guides to determine their understanding of Him. You see, their knowledge of Him will drive their perception of what He has created; therefore, make sure they derive their understanding of Him purely from reason, reaction, fashion, nature, emotion, experience, and imagination (in service to self-exalting desires), but never allow these ways of knowing become subordinate—and certainly not overruled—by that Book.

(17) The Fear of Man

Dear Gorpussel,

Yes, fear is a useful device for leading souls into our Master's domain, but your reference to tempting your subject to fear death reveals ignorance. This kind of provocation, rather than pushing him into the escape of various vices (your list was tedious), can also lead him, by way of concern surrounding the afterlife, straight into the hands of *Him*. Rather than producing direct terror, which is only useful in limited ways under certain circumstances, your efforts should be on the more subtle *fear of man*, which is always beneficial to our cause. By fear of man, I do not necessarily mean the fear of a physical assault, though it may involve this, but the fear of giving offense and suffering under another's displeasure, of being intensely concerned with avoiding any form of conflict to the neglect and denigration of Him. This is the kind of fear to be furnished in the mind of your prey.

(18) Media

Due to the rapid velocity of noise and imagery, the unceasing bombardment of stimulus inherent to certain forms of media, what you will find in your subject, in time, is over-stimulation. In contrast to the lies we've fed the humans regarding their capacities, the animals, by nature, simply cannot handle too much. The effects of excessive stimulation will render your subject less able to read, think, pray and meditate, less willing to resist emotional appeals to the senses, and in many cases, open to more and more intense forms of stimulation, including sinful ones, to keep the drug-like effect going. In accord with our design, electronic media has become the prime narcotic of our age and shows no signs of slowing.

There are other benefits involved with encouraging excessive media consumption in your subject, including the neglect of church and domestic relations as well as an increase in vanity. Hopefully he will also gradually begin to see others as raw material (as all sin does, but some sins more than others), as a means to further his own selfish ends. You see, the form of certain mediums, if they are not careful, begin to slowly work on the brutes, changing their perceptions, isolating them from the relational context, furthering a self-centered fantasy world, until their awareness, concern and regard for others begins to erode or diminish altogether. This temptation can be exploited in many, if not every, form of expression/communication. These others become merely pixels, a disembodied voice, line or two of text, or distant figurine to plaster with petty diatribes. The rewarding fruit of all this can be seen in a culture where dismissing and using each other is accepted and understood, the norm for *consumers*, like drinking a can of soda then tossing it in the trash. All our forecasts see this campaign in media as increasingly beneficial (with certain notable concerns) to enslave the animals and almost entire societies to our cause.

Sincerely,

Senivilous

(19) Gluttony.

To reiterate, gluttony, whether of indulgence or fastidiousness, will briefly satisfy, but in the end prove bitter and the satisfactions will gradually decrease until they are gone, leaving the miseries, deepening his sense of isolation, despair, alienation and hopelessness. This is among the beauties of sin; by its very nature, it eternally destroys while giving only a fleeting, temporal, and diminishing pleasure in return.

(20) Success

Secondly, he must never define success in terms of loving faithfulness and obedience to Him. If he does so, he will be forearmed against some of our most cunning devices. Remember, the culture he inhabits rings with vision after vision of *success*, most of these visions involve perseverance and reliance on the self to achieve some dream. Some of them even involve helping others and may even appear sacrificial, but we know better; ultimately, any work done in the *flesh*, even some great philanthropic endeavor is, at root, selfish. They may even believe they can save themselves; we've been promulgating this lie since time immemorial (one of our most enduring achievements). It's our gospel, the gospel of works! Basically, we tell them they can redeem themselves and establish their own righteousness (and preserve selfishness in the process). One type of vision, particularly prominent in his culture, involves success defined as a heroic struggle and victory against moral inhibitions or traditional values or various controlling forces such as family and religion, only to see the *hero* shuffle off the binding chrysalis and flutter sunward, free and self-fulfilled, determined to do his own will in a world that seeks to enslave. This classic paradigm is just one among the many kinds of visions of success your subject should seek.

Thirdly, another basic principle comes into play here. This tactic overlaps with a previous point but remains distinct and important. Your subject must see success in terms of quantity and numbers and short-term, temporal gain. By the word quantity here, I mean various physical/material attainments: cars, homes, clothes, a sculptured body, vacations, jewelry and stuff like that. This is success in his culture and he must believe it. If he has not been rigorously taught otherwise, this little vision has probably slipped in and rooted itself within his consciousness. How some of the Christians, despite the view of success in that Book and lack of material acquisitions of *Him* when He walked on earth, can still retain this belief, perplexes even us. In some segments of the church, we are quite pleased with the effects of this strategy. Depending on the person, the word quantity could also refer to mental attainments. This can also serve our purposes, but what your subject must never seek is a vision of success involving true spiritual attainments. He must never seek to acquire eternal treasures and crowns and virtues through the self-denial of following Him. In short, he must not seek to pick us his cross, but throw it down as utterly averse towards the fulfillment of his will, his vision. Trick him, make him think he is striving to fulfill a heavenly vision when he is actually following himself, but be careful because He will give them dreams to follow, in that case, make him think the dream is his own and needs to be cast aside. You can often tell which dreams He bestows because they always have the annoying and disgusting tendency to expand His kingdom and testify to it, bringing Him glory.

Sincerely,

Senivilous

(21) Immodesty

It would be best if your subject did not think much about the way people dress at all, but if he does, should regard the immodesty phenomenon as a mere trifle, something insignificant, just one aspect of the fashion of the times. Of course, this promising direction in dress is just one among many practical manifestations of our long and extensive work in that society within the realm of ideas, the region of theory. It's an outworking produced by our educational division, led by Grisalig. And it is most definitely not a simple, fleeting ripple on the surface of society, but reflective of a deep current beneath.

A final note in this letter, which is, admittedly, filled with more theory than practical advice: despite the fact that you will probably experience some resistance in pushing your subject to practice immodesty in his own dress and accept it in others, especially if he spends any time in *that Book* with all its holy and righteous mumbo jumbo, encourage yourself with the fact that one of our greatest successes in this area has been in the church. That vast body of believers in perpetual enmity with us has embraced, in no small measure, worldliness, which I'm pleased to reveal, includes the sweet rank of immodesty.

Sincerely,

(22) Advertisements

Certain advertisements are of great use in furthering vice and denigrating virtue. Make sure you draw his attention to them. Your subject should be among those humans striving to emulate the worldly visions we've cast before their eyes, pursuing not only the attractive physicality of the models, but working to imitate the fashionable "lifestyles" represented.

(23) Celebrity Worship

Beyond congratulating our theorists for their fine work, we must also applaud our many workers toiling in the more practical realm who encourage the acceptance and practice of these ideas. Some of our most brilliant workers can be found in the entertainment industry, where the styles (as well as attitudes and philosophies) embraced by celebrities drive what is accepted by a large portion of the populace, especially the young. You see, the inhabitants of your subject's society regard worldly stars as the elite, and they long to be like them, that is, more specifically, worshiped like them, to be handsome and talented and draw as much attention, applause and earthly treasures towards themselves as possible. One of the ways we've encouraged them to emulate celebrities involves the fact that we have defined success and happiness for them and given them the criteria which determines it. This criterion basically involves solicitations to base self-interest. We've also taught them to see the opposing criteria as expressed in that Book as utterly contemptible, and so it is.

(24) Domestic Abuse

The other party needs little work beyond regular maintenance since he is so steeled against the truth of the dictatorship he's erected by what he would consider his immutable sense of actuality—his undeniable "rightness" in every matter—that your main duty lies in keeping his train of thought steered away from the delightfully ferocious arrogance he possesses. And it doesn't stop there Gorpussel, the domestic environment is merely an arena where the animals are trained in the art of fearing and exploiting each other that these practices may flow over into all their relationships. One can easily foresee the results of this little domestic prep school beyond the borders of their home: The dominated one becomes like a chameleon, changing colors to please all, a puppet responding to each tug of the string, dancing on cue, and the other a bully, sometimes direct, sometimes subtle, depending on the situation, using a vast range of manipulations, controlling with words, tones and looks to force others at the office, the grocery, the bakery, into submission.

(25) Christ's Return

One day our superiority will be fully recognized, that day is forthcoming, our day; don't believe the lies about *His return*. Return for what? It's our world, look at it. Rather than return He's going to keep running away, He's in hiding, fearful of our forces, that's the encouraging report we've received from our superiors working in the deeper recesses beneath us. It's vastly different from the one involving His forthcoming return with its falling stars, blast of a trumpet, receding heavens, innumerable saints and angels and all that bunk, bringing on a flood of fire and judgment. Don't you believe it. If you do, you will become disheartened, discouraged, less profitable in continuing the great work which stands before us. Now I'm well aware that there has, in relation to His so-called return, been a view circulated anonymously (outside the official report on this matter) concerning the "shortness" of our time to conduct our activities and that we must, with regard to the timing and aggressiveness of our plan, figure this short duration possibility into our overall strategy. Whichever view one takes—though, of course, I endorse the official authorized version and encourage others to do so—our approach in this war should always be one of nothing less than extreme, forceful aggression.

(26) Hell

We have the soul of your subject's friend well-gripped in our talons, the man is simply embalmed in luxury and swimming in sin; the real enjoyment for us is forthcoming when all the comforts surrounding him will suddenly be stripped away and he is thrust, shocked and screaming, into the outer darkness.

(27) Heaven

You will find that as your subject's sufferings increase, his desire for heaven—that repellent and garishly luminous place—probably will as well, encouraging him to persist in holiness. This posture must be diverted. Rather than mesmerized with heaven, which makes him a pest on earth, he must be enamored with the earth, making him a pain to heaven and patron to us.

A Pernicious Correspondence

Afterword

A Pernicious Correspondence, beyond the fantastic construct, is basically about the fallen human heart. It's like a journal containing scenes of a voyage through dark topography (not unlike Conrad's classic), though only a small portion because the inner terrain is simply too vast. For this kind of expedition, an exploration into *the effects of the fall and doctrine of sin* was necessary towards the end of helping, by God's grace, to fulfill *The Great Commission*. The specific human heart most often investigated was, of course, my own. Through the process of delving into my own corruption (guided, in part, by Scripture) I think I've acquired, at least, some sense of the sinful desires, thoughts, words, and deeds of humanity in general. Along with this aspect of personal introspection, my observation of others and experiences with them has also been instructive. Still, I prefer to see a significant portion of this little book as a kind of portrait of my soul, a detailed rendering of some of my sinful thoughts, motivations, desires, and actions. It's not a pleasant picture but, I hope, a truthful one. Indeed, it is repulsive, even more loathsome than the final, hideous transformation manifested in the painting of Dorian Gray's visage.

Scott Schuleit
April 27, 2021

Scott Schuleit

SELECT BIBLIOGRAPHY

Lewis, C.S., *The Screwtape Letters*, (New York: Macmillan Publishing Company, 1982)

Within the vast and diverse body of Christian writings over the last several decades, the idea of a fallen angel offering guidance to another in leading human beings into wickedness and, ultimately, hell, has become a kind of little genre of its own. Variations of this idea have appeared in books and articles. The primary literary influence for these works is, of course, *The Screwtape Letters* by C. S. Lewis. For a good portion of the time during the composition of *A Pernicious Correspondence*, this book was on my desk. Previously, it was rather worn, then it became positively tattered, evidenced by an eroding cover and three sections unglued from the binding until, eventually, I had to discard it. I now have another copy of this book. This unique and bedazzling work has been extremely influential in style and content to APC.

Pascal, Blaise, *Pensées*, Translated by A.J. Krailsheimer, (London: Penguin Books, 1995)

This great masterpiece offers profound, incisive meditations on many topics, including human nature. I once heard that Lewis was an avid reader of Pascal. You can see the influence of *Pensées* in *The Screwtape Letters*.

R.C. Sproul, *Legalism*, (*Tabletalk*, February 2011), 4.

Tabletalk is a monthly publication from Ligonier Ministries, a superb Christian parachurch organization which has been a great blessing to me personally. This winsome issue, entitled Letters from the Abyss (complete with exceptional cover art), follows the same format of The Screwtape Letters. It contains letters from senior fallen angels to junior ones on a number of different subjects. R.C. Sproul's letter on legalism was helpful in shaping APC #16.

Reymond, Dr. Robert, L., *A New Systematic Theology of the Christian Faith*, Second Edition— Revised and Updated, (Nashville: Thomas Nelson Publishers, 1998), 442-46.

While reading APC #26 to my wife she noticed an error, leading me to investigate the matter. Her criticism was based on wisdom acquired from Dr. Reymond's fine work. The end result was revision in accordance with insights gained from this excellent one-volume systematic theology.

Rutland, Mark, *Behind the Glittering Mask*, (Ann Arbor: Vine Books, 1996)
This admirable book, structured as a debate on the seven deadly sins between the archangel Michael and Satan, was helpful. It deserves wide reading, not only for its keen insights into human nature and culture, but for its use of the imagination in conveying them.

Acknowledgments

I'm thankful to God for using so many friends and family members in a variety of ways towards the completion of this project. I'm especially grateful to the Lord for my dear wife Christina who has been so supportive, encouraging, and enthusiastic over this work. I've come to respect and appreciate her critical comments, which have often been wise and perceptive, helping to shape the final form of this little book. Thanks darling. Ultimately, of course, anything good can only come from the holy Trinity, therefore, all the errors and anything false in this work is completely on my account and all the good from God, to whom all glory, honor, power, praise, blessing, might and dominion belong. Thank you blessed Father, Son, and Holy Spirit for your great mercy, grace, and kindness to me.

ABOUT THE AUTHOR

Scott Schuleit received the M.A. in Christianity and Culture from Knox Theological Seminary. He has served as a teacher in a classical school, youth ministry leader, and adjunct instructor at a Christian college. Currently, he is the Associate Pastor at Taft Street Baptist Church in Pembroke Pines, FL. His non-fiction has been published in several print and non-print publications, including: Tabletalk, Reformed Perspectives Magazine, Monergism.com, The Gospel Coalition, and Modern Reformation. His poems have appeared in several publications, including: The Penwood Review, Critique, and Christianity and Literature. Also, a work of short fiction was published in Reformed Perspectives Magazine entitled Paradise and Perdition: An Exploration through Narrative Theology into the Interior of Two Doctrines.

A Pernicious Correspondence is his first published book. He enjoys teaching, preaching, the arts, theology, and spending time with his dear wife Christina. Scott may be contacted through the publisher at:
publisher@prevailpress.com.